North Atlantic Policy –
The Agricultural Gap

North Atlantic Policy –

The Agricultural Gap

JOHN O. COPPOCK

 The Twentieth Century Fund
New York 1963

Foreword

The Twentieth Century Fund has long been concerned with the progress of integration in Europe and in the wider Atlantic community. It could not fail, therefore, to be concerned with the formidable obstacle which nationalist agricultural policies have placed in the way of a more rapid advance and more complete economic unification. An opportunity to explore the difficulty and the possibilities of a constructive agricultural policy was presented by John Coppock at the close of his association with J. Frederic Dewhurst in the writing of *Europe's Needs and Resources* (1961). The Fund is grateful to Mr. Coppock for the care with which he has pursued the resulting inquiry.

In recent months political impediments to European unity have assumed a larger place than the economic problems of agriculture. But the latter will remain, when perhaps the political climate has grown more favorable. To consider the issues calmly and to see the possibilities in a mood of moderate hope can be useful now, and can open new doorways in the next years. That this study may be a contribution to the cause of Atlantic cooperation is the hope of the author as it is of the Twentieth Century Fund.

AUGUST HECKSCHER, *Director*
The Twentieth Century Fund

41 East 70th Street, New York
April 1963

Preface

Since this study was completed, the President of the French Fifth Republic has displaced agriculture as the chief obstacle to progress toward unification of Western Europe and a firmly rooted Atlantic partnership. The displacement is likely to be temporary. French governments come and go: agricultural problems, like France, are eternal — or so they appear to be. They will almost certainly regain the dubious distinction of being a major stumbling block in the path of Atlantic integration.

This study attempts to analyze why so many difficulties are encountered in the field of agriculture by those attempting to create an Atlantic community. It tries to look a few years into the future to see what might happen if present agricultural policies are continued. Perhaps optimistically, it suggests that "all is not lost" — that there are some self-correcting forces at work. Governments can adopt policies in support of those forces to strengthen them and to bring their beneficial effects sooner than if left to their own momentum. Governments can, in most countries, take these actions without serious risk to their political necks.

European unity and greater Atlantic integration would be one of the great events in history. To jeopardize it, even to slow its arrival, by disagreement over agricultural policies is an act of political irresponsibility. Each of the countries in the North Atlantic region has its own agricultural problems. In essence, they are similar in kind and they spring from similar sources. They must be solved and there is little reason to believe that they can be solved more easily on a national basis than in an international framework.

This thesis is not new. The problems of agriculture have elicited an enormous volume of written words in recent years. The author would be much surprised if most readers do not remark to themselves, "I have read this before." He hopes only that many familiar facts have been brought together in a manner which will make clearer the international aspects of the problems, the relative magnitudes of them in different countries and some of the political strains which will have to be faced if they are to be solved in a way which will make agriculture a worthy partner of industry in a more integrated Atlantic community.

The reader of this study merits a warning as to what it is not concerned with. It is not about the problems of world agriculture, "hunger in the midst of plenty," and what we must do to help improve agriculture in the poorer parts of the world. These are matters of prime importance and deserve intensive study, not to mention more enlightened government policies in the conduct of our foreign aid programs. But they are not the subject of this volume. This study is limited to the problems of agriculture which have arisen from politics and economics in the industrialized countries of the West. Their potential power to block integration of those countries into an effective Atlantic partnership is great — and if more integration is not achieved the bad effects will fall on all, rich and poor countries alike.

The absence of discussion of the problems of tobacco, cotton, wool and other "industrial" farm products is intentional. The study is limited to a review of the situation for nontropical foods — the commodities produced in all, or nearly all, of the countries under consideration. It is an analysis of the conflict between producers and their government sponsors. Tobacco and fibers play a small part in this context, important as they are to agriculture in the United States.

The reader may wonder why the mid–1950s has been selected for much of the analysis and the base period for projections. More recent data are certainly available. However, the middle years of the 1950s displayed two characteristics which make them useful as a base period. In Western Europe they were years when a temporary plateau was reached with respect to agricultural production and a diminution in the earlier rapid rate of increased food consumption. In the United States and Canada this was a period of reasonable farm prosperity, but it precedes the years when large surpluses began to be accumulated. It is a period as "normal" as one can select.

To the fullest extent possible this study is based on published documents originating with international organizations. Other writers — literally hundreds of them — have studied the same documents and have drawn conclusions similar to or widely divergent from those in this study. While few of them are mentioned, the author owes a major debt to those whom he has read.

Thanks are also due to numerous officials of the U. S. Department of Agriculture and the British Ministry of Agriculture, Fisheries and Food; to the Washington offices of the Food and Agriculture Organization and the European Economic Community; to members of the staffs of the Economic Commission for Europe and its combined Food and Agriculture Organization – ECE Agriculture Division in Geneva; to the staff of the Organisation for European Economic Cooperation in Paris; to many individuals elsewhere who contributed ideas and opposed some held by the author.

Special thanks are due Mr. P. Lamartine Yates, Dr. Mordecai Ezekiel and Dr. Isador Lubin, who read the manuscript with varying degrees of disapproval but whose suggestions were all of great assistance. And, of course, the author is grateful to the Directors and Trustees of the Twentieth Century Fund for making the study possible.

Mrs. Frances Klafter, as editor, worked tirelessly with the manuscript to bring order out of confusion. Mrs. Sara Sklar typed most of the manuscript and, with my wife, Joan Coppock, prepared it for the printer. It is not possible to express adequately my appreciation of their work.

JOHN O. COPPOCK

Washington, D.C.
March 1963

Contents

North Atlantic Policy –
The Agricultural Gap

CHAPTER

1

Economic Integration and Autarkic Agriculture

The economic (and perhaps the political) historian of the future may look back on 1961 as one of the "great years." He may find that the United Kingdom, in applying for membership in the European Economic Community, set in motion a new force in the drive for integration, a force not to be spent until it had encompassed North America and extended far across the Pacific to Australia and New Zealand, thus giving a new framework to the economic and political aspects of Western civilization.

If the historian can make this happy evaluation, he may find it necessary to note that this historic sequence of events almost failed to take place; that the series of negotiations which brought it about nearly foundered on the difficulties of reaching a mutual understanding on agricultural policies; that over many months of negotiations it seemed that a half billion people — the best-fed in the world — might be deprived of the benefits of economic integration, because their governments could not reach agreement on how to meet the diverse points of view of legislators and organizations speaking for 15 million farmers and their families; that in the end, however, good sense prevailed and the problems of agriculture proved to be not so difficult to solve as had been feared.

Without benefit of the historian's hindsight the negotiators of an expanding Atlantic community will find, as the six original members of the Common Market have found, that conflicts regarding agriculture are among the most difficult to reconcile of the myriad clashes of interest which attend peaceable economic unification. The reasons why agricultural unification poses particularly intractable problems are not difficult to isolate. The rise of the movement toward economic integration in the 1950s in Western Europe coincided with a belated arrival of the technological revolution in agriculture. In the fifteen years following World War II European agriculture underwent greater changes in methods of production than it had experienced in the preceding century — and the end was not in sight. In a few short years much of Europe's farming was changed from a kind of handicraft to an industrial operation.[1]

The postwar period was one of great industrial growth in most of the countries of Western Europe and (to less extent) North America, and nonagricultural employment opportunities were generally good. Nevertheless, had the revolution in agricultural techniques been allowed to have its full impact, redundant agricultural workers would have posed serious employment problems in most countries. It is true that farm populations fell nearly everywhere, and in some countries (Germany, Sweden and the United States) fell at a rapid pace. Nearly every industrialized society witnessed a drift of hired labor and young members of farm families to nonfarm jobs.

But the numbers of small farm operators, particularly in continental Europe, were very great. Many of them were ill-prepared to obtain other employment. Technological potentials in agriculture called for a vast consolidation and restructuring of farm holdings. Social conscience and practical politics combined to produce government policies which would slow the exodus from farming.

Ameliorating the human distress which would have resulted from a forced exodus from agriculture at a more rapid rate, however,

1. There are notable exceptions to these generalizations, particularly in Denmark, the Netherlands and the United Kingdom, where the process of accepting modern techniques in agriculture began much earlier and evolved more gradually. In most of the rest of Western Europe, especially in the three large countries — France, Germany and Italy — modern farming before World War II was the exception, not the rule.

raised other serious problems. In very simple terms, governments supported farm prices in order to permit more farmers than needed to remain on the land and still have tolerably good incomes. In the process of doing this they almost automatically assured rapid increases in output. Moreover, governments adopted policies which largely sealed off their own farmers from foreign competition. The chief result was the progressive development of surpluses. In the traditional exporting countries the surpluses began to appear in physical form. In the importing countries in Europe the economic equivalent of surpluses appeared in the form of high prices consumers had to pay to their agricultural compatriots for an increasing part of their food needs — prices much higher than they would have had to pay had they been able to buy freely abroad.

All this did not happen at once, of course. As the next chapter shows, agricultural protectionism has been a facet of economic policies in most countries for many years. What was new about the situation was the growing intensity of protective measures for agriculture in an international situation which was moving toward more integration and international competition in nonagricultural goods. For the earnest men and women trying to build a European community, perhaps an Atlantic community, the question of national agricultural policies posed a continuing threat to the success of their efforts.

No problem has seemed so nearly insoluble as that of agriculture in the various international forums in which freer trading arrangements have been sought in recent years. The General Agreement on Tariffs and Trade (GATT) has been of almost no influence in obtaining reductions in agricultural protectionism, despite its rather creditable record of establishing more competitive conditions for industrial products. The member countries of the Organisation for European Economic Cooperation (OEEC), once the worst of their balance-of-payments difficulties had been eased, established a "code of liberalization" aimed at a progressive reduction in restraints on trade between the members. Agricultural products lagged far behind other commodities in coming under the code. At no time did this remarkable European organization take the same kind of hard, penetrating look at agriculture that it did, for example, at energy materials and steel. The so-called "Green Plan," proposed by France in the early 1950s to focus the power of the OEEC on European agriculture as a whole, failed to attract enough support to produce anything except a continuing interministerial committee whose main function has been limited to producing a series of five useful reports over the past decade.

The most ambitious effort toward economic integration in recent years was, of course, the formation of the European Economic Community, comprising Belgium, France, Germany, Italy, Luxembourg and the Netherlands. While the drafters of the Treaty of Rome (the basic document establishing the Community) were able to reach very nearly complete agreement on most matters concerning industry, they were forced to leave the sections dealing with agriculture vague and undefined. Four years after the signing of the treaty — and a year and a half after a special intergovernmental committee had turned in its proposals for a common agricultural policy — the member countries were still able to reach only general agreement on the specific actions which would bring the agricultural provisions of the treaty into force. We will return to this point later.

Agricultural problems were major obstacles — though not the only ones — confronting members of the Community and the other European countries in the late 1950s in the long negotiations which failed to produce a free-trade area — a customs union to all intents and purposes — comprising all OEEC members. In the subsequent negotiations between Austria, Denmark, Norway, Portugal, Sweden, Switzerland and the United Kingdom, which established the European Free Trade Association (EFTA), agriculture was specifically exempted from the automatic trade-freeing provisions contained in the agreement for industrial products.

The United Kingdom's decision in 1961 to apply for membership in the Common Market was made dependent on reaching agreement concerning agriculture with the original six EEC members, not for Britain alone but for the other members of the EFTA who might wish to join or associate themselves with the EEC. Britain also promised satisfactory arrangements for other members of the Commonwealth.

Agriculture was again found to be at the center of a serious international disagreement when the EEC, having adopted a common tariff which raised some national rates, undertook negotiations with its fellow members of GATT to provide compensatory adjustments. The negotiations for these tariff modifications, required before another round of mutual tariff-reducing concessions could be attempted, ended with a nearly complete stalemate with respect to a number of important agricultural products.

INTEGRATION AND DISCRIMINATION

For more than a decade the United States government has urged greater economic integration in Western Europe. The European Coal and Steel Community and the European Economic Community itself owe a not inconsequential debt to steady support for their formation from across the Atlantic.

The political burden involved in supporting a form of European integration which can effectively discriminate against American exports to Europe has never been a light one for any American administration — Truman's, Eisenhower's or Kennedy's. The justifications for supporting this development, while changing in emphasis from time to time, have not greatly varied. Economic unification is a good thing in itself; in no other way is it likely that a trading area could have been formed which would be large enough and free enough to form the basis for modern, mass-production industry. Economic unification — and the economic growth which accompanies it — is a desirable adjunct of Western military solidarity; it provides the strong economic foundation on which an adequate defensive alliance can be maintained. Finally, economic unification will bring in its train political unity, thus ending all fears of a recrudescence of the traditional quarrels of the nations of Western Europe.

Armed with these arguments, the American administrations of the past decade have been able to overcome the arguments of those critical of the policy of support for European unification. The criticisms have been varied. Those which are essentially economic have usually centered on the problem of discrimination against

American exports — that a European common market would mean tariffs against American exports to, say, France, while German exports would be admitted duty free. To this the usual reply has been that unification would so greatly expand the economy of Europe that there would be a greater potential market for American exports. We had overcome tariffs in our trading with individual European countries; surely in a much more prosperous unified Europe we could do as well with whatever tariffs they might establish in common.

Behind this line of argument lay an assumption that protectionism in a common market would be modest. As the area of "exclusion" expanded, the degree of exclusion would be reduced. No other outcome would be feasible. A strongly protected European common market would split the West into trade blocs with so little economic intercourse and such intense rivalry in third areas of the world that other fundamental aspects of Western unity would be endangered.

Such was the basis for the trade expansion legislation offered the Congress in early 1962: we have achieved the desired economic integration of Europe by tolerating the actual and latent discrimination against American trade that it implied. Now let us get back to Geneva and take up under GATT where we left off in our efforts to reduce levels of protection on a reciprocal basis. Let us get on with creating something new under the sun — a world economy in which goods move (at least between industrialized countries) virtually unhampered by tariffs.

Armed with broad permissive legislation not riddled by too many exceptions and escape clauses, the negotiators of the next round of mutual concessions may well make tremendous progress in the direction of freer trade — except for agricultural products.[2] The

2. The early indications are that the products of a number of industries will escape the net of "across-the-board" concessions. However, agricultural products represent one of the few classes of goods which one part of the industrialized North Atlantic region will insist on special protection against from another part of the same region. For manufactures, such as textiles, exceptional protection (not necessarily in the form of tariffs) is generally asked in the name of defense against "low-wage" producers. Petroleum (and perhaps coal) stands in a class by itself and it can be expected that it will be treated as a nearly separate problem.

member countries of the EEC, by adopting the kind of agricultural policy proposed to them by their Commission, served notice on the rest of the free world that agriculture was a "thing apart" from the generally liberal economic organization being developed on the basis of the Treaty of Rome. And the Commission, in proposing an agricultural policy with rigid controls over international trade, was being realistic. It was fully aware that it could put in jeopardy the whole structure of European economic unification if it attempted to press adoption of a policy for agriculture which matched in freedom and liberality the plans for industry.

THE TREATY AND THE COMMON POLICY

It is necessary to understand what the common agricultural policy of the EEC, developed out of a confusing and obfuscated part of the Treaty of Rome, really is. It is discouraging to anyone who might have hope that agriculture will take its place in what promises to be an unprecedented advance in the direction of freer trading arrangements in the noncommunist part of the world. It represents a sort of anchor point from which the prospective flow of the tide in international agricultural matters may be measured. Unsatisfactory as it is from the standpoint of a sensible international division of effort, it still represents the only coherent statement of intent with respect to agriculture to emanate from any country or group of countries in this period of radical changes in international economic policies. As such it will be the starting point for what must be in store — a protracted period of international negotiations to bring agriculture back at least part way to the discipline of international competition.

In ten articles covering nine pages of the treaty, the EEC members agree that the Common Market should extend to agriculture (Article 38) but assure each member that the minimum prices to be established "shall not be such as to lead to a reduction of exchanges existing between Member States . . ." (Article 44). After stating that there will be common rules concerning competition (Article 40), the treaty goes on to say that the general rules of competition in the Community "shall apply to the production of and trade in agricultural products only to the extent determined by the Council within the framework of the provisions and in accordance with the procedure laid down in Article 43," which puts off official consideration of the whole problem for the first two years after the treaty comes into force and provides some loopholes in the eventual organizational structure (Article 42). But Article 43 then says that exceptions to the general rules governing competition should be made in the light of "the objectives mentioned in Article 39," which include ensuring "a fair standard of living for the agricultural population" and action "to stabilise markets," while taking account of "the particular character of agricultural activities, arising from the social structure of agriculture and from structural and natural disparities between the various agricultural regions" and "the need to make the appropriate adjustments gradually; . . ."[3]

The treaty provisions for agriculture leave the impression that there should be a common market for agriculture as long as it does not embarrass any member government politically in its dealings with its farmer constituents. The job of fitting this square peg into a round hole was turned over to a committee, acting for the Commission of the EEC, whose instructions were to draw up specific proposals before June 30, 1960. The committee produced a voluminous report exactly on time.[4]

This report, with certain modifications, formed the basis for the common agricultural policy finally adopted by the six members of the EEC in January 1962. It constitutes a rigid, autarkic plan for the control of agriculture within the EEC. Unmodified it may provide an enormous obstacle to further progress toward economic integration in the North Atlantic region.

In essence the common agricultural policy calls for the achievement by the end of the decade of a system of unified prices throughout the Community for every important agricultural product grown in Western Europe. "Target prices" will be established, probably

3. Secretariat of the Interim Committee for the Common Market and Euratom, *Treaty Establishing the European Economic Community and Connected Documents,* Brussels, 1957.

4. EEC Commission, *Proposals for the Working-Out and Putting into Effect of the Common Agricultural Policy in Application of Article 43 of the Treaty Establishing the European Economic Community,* Brussels, June 30, 1960, mimeo.

annually. The actual price may deviate somewhat from the target, but if the price falls below the target by a prescribed per cent (probably 5 to 7 per cent) appropriate boards operated by the EEC Commission will be required to "intervene." Such intervention can take the form of withholding products from the market through board purchases and suspending import licenses.

Unless such intervention is in force, import licenses are to be granted freely. However, imports will be subject to a "variable levy" (sometimes in conjunction with a tariff and minimum import prices) which will be the difference between the target price and "the most favourable buying terms on the external market." Application of this levy (more familiarly known in the United States as an "equalization fee") simply insulates the Common Market from all external competition. No amount of price reduction, whether it originates from export subsidization or from normal market developments in the exporting countries, will assist exporters to penetrate the EEC market.

This aspect of the common agricultural policy does not, in fact, add importantly to the sum of protection given European agriculture in recent years. Indeed, when and if the policy is fully operative toward the end of the present decade, it may at least amount to an increase in competition within the Common Market — a point to which various member governments, present and prospective, were not oblivious during the negotiations leading to the agreement. The really important aspect of this part of the policy is that it formalizes, in an announced policy agreement having the force of a treaty, the intention of the countries subscribing to the policy to seal off permanently and irrevocably the market for most temperate agricultural products. No other long-term proposal under the Treaty of Rome can approach this in terms of declared autarkical intentions.

The only "loopholes," if they can be called that, in this rigid system of agricultural protectionism are the prices to be chosen for targets in the EEC market and for intervention by the marketing authorities. They could be set at, or progressively move toward, relatively modest levels. This might inhibit increases in internal production in the EEC area sufficiently for a large volume of imports to continue to be required. Alternatively, the prices could be — and, initially at least, probably will be — established at levels well above those which would have to be paid for imported supplies of many products. Given the political strength of farmers in Europe, the latter course would seem most likely.

What, if anything, might limit this tendency toward high prices?

The basic restraints are two, and it is difficult to forecast how effective they will be. The first is the prospect that high prices would induce physical surpluses, bringing the EEC as a whole into the muddle so familiar to Americans. EEC policies require that when the intervention price of a commodity is reached import licensing be suspended and the commodity boards support the price by purchases and by withholding supplies from the market. The experts drawing up the proposed policies were aware of the problem of surpluses but they failed to be very specific with respect to what should be done about it. Small wonder, given the conflicting treaty provisions their proposed system was asked to implement![5]

> In view of the difficulties which would arise from a state of permanent overproduction, the common policy will have to aim at balance between production and potential outlets both in and outside the Community.

And,

> Imports and exports in the external trade of the Community with non-member countries must also be given due weight when working out the market policy.

But,

> Agricultural policy . . . must ensure that the value attached to agricultural products is such that it helps to guarantee to farming activities a fair remuneration approaching that obtained in the other sectors of the economy.

What prices will this require?

> The final common level to be reached will be fixed in the light of the repercussions of the first stages of approximation in the various regions and types of enterprise and by adaptation to the trend of agri-

5. EEC Commission, *op. cit.*, pars. 37–43. Quotations in subsequent paragraphs are also from this source.

cultural markets as a whole and to the general economic situation in the Community countries.

This is not very specific, but

Account will also have to be taken of the fact that the conditions of production and the characteristics of farms in the Community differ from those in the extra-European countries which are large-scale agricultural exporters. In addition, the prices of agricultural products on the world market are still frequently distorted by artificial measures. This is why, generally speaking, prices for agricultural produce cannot be on the same level within the Community as those at present obtaining on the world market, but must be stabilised at a higher level.

The policy makers thus foresee at least the possibility, even the probability, of physical surpluses. So they look abroad for some of their markets. They pay due heed to the fact that they are committed, as a Community, to respect international agreements, but they recall that "due regard must be paid to the necessity of maintaining commercial exchanges and contractual links of a political and economic nature with nonmember countries." They also believe that "the common agricultural policy will have, moreover, to be such that it can stimulate exports of agricultural products." Even so, prices inside the Community are going to be higher than world prices, for they must maintain the level of agricultural incomes. Thus "it is essential not to expose the agricultural production of the Community to the full blast of competition from the world market; . . ."

If the prices inside the Community are high enough to provide adequate incomes, they are likely to be high enough to induce surpluses. How do such surpluses get marketed abroad? For every important commodity the policy proposes "to make exporting possible through refunds on exports corresponding to the charges made on imports."

Since the charges made on imports — the levy — represent the difference between the (probably high) target price inside the Community and the lowest, "most favourable buying terms on the external market," it is obvious that exports benefiting from such "refunds" will be competitive with the lowest prices, subsidized or

unsubsidized, on the world market. The European producer, however, will receive the full target price (or perhaps intervention
price). Thus does the EEC propose to join officially the band of
export dumpers — the same group whose actions on the world
market are said to be partially responsible for the Community's need
to isolate its producers from foreign competition.

The prospect of surpluses may tend to hold target prices in the
Community down, not because there is no mechanism for disposing
of surpluses, but because it will be costly. The cost, however, may
not be too much of a deterrent. The policy proposes the establish-
ment of a "Guidance and Guarantee Fund," with subsections for
particular commodities, which will be financed by proceeds of the
import levies, taxes on producers, contributions by governments and
"perhaps also by other resources." Apparently the real cost of subsidizing exports, actually borne by the ultimate consumers within
the Community, will be fairly tidily hidden away from public view.
Presumably only government contributions to the fund will have to
pass through legislative review and be appropriated by the member
governments.

The second pressure which may keep prices within the Community not greatly in excess of external prices is of a much broader
sort. Food purchases are a large element in total personal consumption expenditures in even the most prosperous of the EEC countries. A substantial rise in food prices, reflecting higher farm prices,
would have a perceptible impact on the cost of living of nonfarm
families. This unquestionably would be reflected in wage demands
— a matter of considerable importance to industry, heavily involved in producing and shipping industrial goods to competitive export markets. Wage increases might well have an adverse effect on
the competitive position abroad of industries whose products have a
large labor-cost component.

This might be thought of as a difficulty which would affect, during a temporary period of adjustment, only those countries in which
farm prices are now relatively low — the Netherlands and France.
In fact, it is a continuing problem of some magnitude in all countries. If farm prices are high enough to provide farm incomes reasonably comparable with nonfarm incomes, they will be high

enough to keep too many farmers on the land. With an expected rapid growth in nonagricultural productivity, "fair" incomes for farmers in relation to urban workers will rise regardless of the comparative efficiency of farming. Deprived in part of one of its main reasons for improvement — the rapid decline in farm population — farm productivity is unlikely to rise as rapidly as nonfarm productivity. Thus the pressure by farmers for regular increases in target prices will be considerable.

At the same time, however, the inarticulate consumer in the EEC may be joined by the very articulate industrialist in an effort to keep the level of target prices not too much above external prices. Whether the resistance will be successful is, of course, another matter.

In the relatively short run, during the period of transition in which the common agricultural policy will come into force gradually and national differences in prices will be progressively reduced, it is probably safe to predict that prices for the main agricultural products will be high. They may not be so high as those prevailing recently in Germany (where they have bordered on the ridiculous compared to world market prices), Italy and Belgium, but they are likely to be as high as or higher than recent French prices and higher than some Dutch prices.

BRITISH ACCESSION TO THE MARKET

The great unknown factor with respect to the future workings of the common agricultural policy of the EEC is what the effect of the United Kingdom's membership might be. (Of course, the accession of other countries, notably Denmark, would have an impact on the manner in which a common agricultural policy would be administered in a broadened EEC; however, the United Kingdom's importance as an importer of temperate products, together with its pledge to secure appropriate terms for EEC membership of its fellow members of the European Free Trade Association, makes Britain the focal point of any negotiations to modify the common agricultural policy agreed upon by the original six members.)

The United Kingdom, more than any other country, has a large economic stake in retaining access to low-cost temperate agricultural products. Producing at home little more than half its requirements of such products, it is heavily dependent on imports which it must presumably seek to obtain at favorable prices. Moreover, it has numerous commitments of long standing — which are political as well as economic — to members of the Commonwealth, assuring markets for their agricultural products: cereals from Canada; cereals, fruit, sugar and meat from Australia; butter and meat from New Zealand; sugar from the British West Indies.

From the time of its formal application for membership in the EEC in the autumn of 1961 Britain has steadfastly reassured the original members, particularly France, of its willingness to accept completely a common agricultural policy. What in fact the British government means by this is difficult to ascertain. The promise was made before the original six members finally agreed on a policy. Even if it were the custom of British diplomacy to sign blank checks, it is unlikely one of this magnitude would be so freely offered. A conservative estimate is that British imports of food and feedstuff in recent volume and at prices prevailing in France (the lowest that can be expected under the common agricultural pricing mechanism) would raise the British import bill, in terms of entry prices, by more than $1 billion annually. While expanded British production might be expected to reduce the demand for imports somewhat, there can be no question that a common agricultural policy as now planned, with the prices which are in prospect, would seriously worsen Britain's international trade balance, if exporters raised their prices to European levels.

The impact on the balance of payments is not the only problem that the common agricultural policy as it has been agreed by the original six members of the EEC would pose for the United Kingdom. Market prices in Britain for most agricultural products are based on prices of imported commodities, which carry rather modest tariffs or, like wheat, none. Income supports for British farmers are granted in the form of deficiency payments — the difference between the average price farmers actually receive in selling in competition with imports and an agreed price they "should" receive, which is established at an annual price review. In recent years these deficiency payments, along with certain other subsidies which will be proscribed under the common agricultural policy, have approached $1 billion, paid from appropriated funds.

The common agricultural policy bars the use of this price-supporting technique. Thus, if it is applied to the United Kingdom, market prices will rise sharply. The budget will be relieved of the cost of the deficiency payments and most other subsidies, but the consumer will pay at least the same amount — perhaps considerably more — in additional expenditures over the counter. The effect of this on the cost of living in the United Kingdom should not be overestimated, of course. The cost of unprocessed food at the farm gate or at the port is a limited part of the consumer price of food, and food expenditures are less than a third of total private spending. Nevertheless, the higher food prices will mean a perceptible change in the cost of living and could well give rise to additional pressure for higher wages — a problem which has constantly plagued the British economy over the past decade.

In varying degrees the same problem faces other countries which might join or become associated with the Common Market. For some, however, the chief difficulty in accession to the EEC takes a different form. In Denmark and Ireland important proportions of the agricultural industries are organized around the importation of low-cost cereals and other feedstuffs and the export — mainly to the United Kingdom — of livestock products at relatively low prices. If the common agricultural policy operates effectively, viewed from the standpoint of the other member countries (though not the Netherlands, which faces much the same problem as Denmark and Ireland), this pattern of production and trade will be modified greatly. Access to cheap feedstuffs from overseas will be restricted[6] and price competition within the Common Market area will all but disappear. Danish, Irish and Dutch producers of livestock products will receive in general somewhat higher prices, both at home and in other EEC countries — sufficiently higher to provide them with more profit per unit of production. They will obtain such a benefit, however, by jeopardizing expansion — or even

6. Except for those used to produce livestock products to be sold outside the Common Market, for which a complicated system of rebates is planned.

maintenance — of their markets. Despite the protestation of the Treaty of Rome (Article 44) that the minimum prices adopted under the common policy "shall not be such as to lead to a reduction of exchanges between the Member States," the virtual elimination of any threat of price competition can scarcely fail to elicit more output from less efficient producers. The classic characteristics and problems of a cartel are clearly visible in this situation.

The formation of a unified agricultural market (with many of the attributes of a cartel) from components having widely different national structures and interests is beset with almost insuperable difficulties, as shown in the negotiations leading to agreement of the original six members of the EEC. The big guns of the negotiating armory, extending far outside the field of agriculture itself, were hauled into place and prepared for firing. France threatened to refuse to permit the EEC as a whole to enter the second phase of the transition period, which can be described without much exaggeration as a point of no return. Mutterings were heard from Germany, with twin interests in very high internal prices for its farmers and low import prices for its urban consumers, that it should league with the United Kingdom — with similar interests — to reach a substantially different arrangement for agriculture from that proposed in the EEC. That view did not prevail.

In the event, the French won the negotiating battle in Brussels over the winter of 1961–62. They got most of what they asked for — a completely insulated internal EEC market in which they can, by careful and continuous maneuvering and negotiation, lay first claim to any expansion of requirements within the market and, over time, displace imports from outside the area.

THE TRADITIONAL SUPPLIERS

To win the battle but lose the war is a familiar phenomenon of history, including that of France. It is too early to say with certainty that this victory in agricultural policy will in fact "stay won." One thing is certain: the traditional suppliers of temperate agricultural products to Western Europe have become progressively more disturbed as French intentions to "steal" their markets have become more clearly understood. They may or may not be able to translate their displeasure into effective preventive action. They will almost certainly try — in direct agricultural negotiation and in the context of more general negotiations on economic, financial and trade relations.

The United States, Canada, Australia, New Zealand and Argentina are the chief suppliers on the international market of the most important temperate food products — bread grains, coarse grains for feed and livestock products.[7] Western Europe, particularly the United Kingdom and Germany, constitutes a very large part of the world commercial market for the portion of these commodities which enters into international trade.

Apart from Argentina, the large exporting countries could look with a fair degree of equanimity on the consolidation of the original six members of the EEC into a single protected market. All of the six except the Netherlands were already quite protectionist in their national agricultural policies. It was true, of course, that the prospect of seeing France take over the rather substantial German market for cereals was not a pleasant one. However, the Franco-German agreement of 1959, which made this intention clear, was generally looked upon as part of the price the rest of the West would have to pay to assure that the Common Market became a working organism. No loud objections were heard.

The decision of the United Kingdom in the summer of 1961 to apply for membership in the EEC put a new face on the matter. Britain is the great prize in international trade in temperate agricultural products. It requires imports sufficient to feed about 25 million people — nearly as many as the combined populations of Canada, Australia and New Zealand, fellow members of the British Commonwealth from which Britain buys a large part of its requirements.

The momentous British decision coincided with a growing comprehension of some other facts about European agriculture. The

7. As indicated earlier, Denmark, Ireland and the Netherlands are large exporters of livestock products. However, as substantial importers of feedstuffs, they must be thought of as "fabricators-in-transit" — importing raw materials and exporting finished products.

full implications of the proposed common agricultural policy drawn up by the EEC Commission in 1960 were suddenly impressed on the governments of the traditional supplying countries. At the same time the statistics of agricultural production in Europe made it clear that the technological revolution was far from over. Farm output, after a deceptive lull in the middle years of the 1950s, had begun again to rise rapidly. And another set of statistics was equally disturbing. The rapid growth in per capita food consumption which had characterized the postwar period had begun to taper off. The burgeoning market which had been able to absorb both greatly expanded domestic production and a large volume of imports was seen to be growing at a much slower rate by the end of the 1950s, while home output continued to increase.

In this context of a rigidly protectionist EEC agricultural policy, a proved capacity for expanded production behind the walls of the protected market and a diminishing rate of growth of the market itself the prospect of British accession to the EEC took on an ominous aspect for the traditional suppliers. True, the United Kingdom had promised the Commonwealth countries that their interests would be protected as the British negotiated for EEC membership. But the promise does not really fit the facts of the situation. At best, it implies that the other members of the EEC would be willing — if Britain desired — to permit the Commonwealth countries to maintain for a period of time a growing proportion of a shrinking European market, at the expense of the United States and Argentina. That prospect is not a happy one and is unlikely to be realized.

The hard underlying fact of the situation is that continental Europe is rapidly approaching a point of self-sufficiency plus exportable surpluses of many temperate food products, as a result of national policies which could have had no other result. The EEC has now declared its intention to continue, even intensify, its agricultural protectionism. Britain, having chosen to become "European," will be expected by the EEC — and particularly France — to take the bitter with the sweet. If Britain wants to sell its manufactures inside a protected market, it will have to buy its food inside that market — as long as that is a rule of the game to which the other members subscribe.

The only real course for Britain — and other countries in a similar position — is to battle for a modification of the common policy or for administration of it in a manner which would lessen its autarkic aspects. In the long run, of course, such a modification would be good for all of the EEC. Paying more than is necessary for food, produced at home or abroad, makes very little economic sense. As will be seen, an ex-farmer in a factory is worth a good deal more to the economy in most countries in Europe (as well as the United States) than a farmer in a field. But right now farmers, in all their numbers, are in the field — a fact that receives widespread political recognition.

The common agricultural policy of the EEC is nearly the final word in autarky. In a sense it is an "improved" form of protectionism, consolidating the hodgepodge of protectionist devices which have marked national agricultural policies of most countries for a long time. To understand why this economically illiberal policy must mar the image of the great advance toward economic rationalization represented by the EEC, we must look to its antecedents and the reasons for their existence. Only then will it be possible to judge whether the policy is immutable or susceptible to modification.

2

Government Management of Agriculture

World agriculture in the mid-twentieth century is basically "out of kilter." Mankind's most basic industry — working the soil to obtain food and fiber — is being operated in a socially unsatisfactory manner in virtually every part of the earth. In Asia, Africa and parts of Latin America there are more hungry people than at any other time in history. If recent experience is a guide, there will be even more hunger-ridden millions before agricultural systems in these areas are modernized sufficiently to be able to produce the minimum requirements of the populations in these regions.

In North America, Australasia and parts of Western Europe agricultural output is more than sufficient to meet the needs of the populations. A recent phenomenon in agriculture — unsalable surpluses — has now become a commonplace in these regions. Large amounts of agricultural produce are withheld from the market and vast areas of usable land are left uncultivated.

Mismanagement in agriculture is widespread in the free world, but it is not a peculiarity of capitalist countries or of democratic countries. By all accounts the Soviet Union has dismantled one form of agricultural management, not a very good one, without being able to replace it by an effective "reform" of a socialist sort. The virtual disappearance of Russian wheat from the international market after World War I was not accompanied by an increase in domestic consumption and the cities suffered from reduced supplies. Management of agriculture in the Soviet Union has undergone a series of reforms without notable success in solving its problems.[1] The organization of Chinese agriculture on a communal basis is generally held to be at least partially responsible for the nearly disastrous food shortages in that country in 1959–1961. In Eastern Europe

> ... agriculture failed to achieve the progress planned for it. Whereas by mid-1953 industrial production was, on the average, about double the pre-war volume, agricultural output was still below the pre-war level. ...
>
> Although the controls over eastern European agricultural production appeared to form a carefully conceived system, they did not operate satisfactorily in practice.[2]

Agricultural mismanagement in most of the countries of the North Atlantic region, however, is of a different kind from that experienced in most of the countries of the Soviet bloc and China. There — and in many noncommunist countries as well — the problem has been to end either quasi-feudal or inefficient peasant organization of agriculture without disrupting the production and marketing of farm output. In most of the Western countries the problem has been the rationalization, in a manner which would reflect better economic utilization of resources, of an industry already producing a large volume of goods.

It must be said that the management of Western agriculture, judged by this economic criterion, has been a failure. On the face of it, there are few economic phenomena to match in absurdity the piling up of huge surpluses of agricultural products in the United States over the past decade; or the continued production of inferior

1. The latest of these was the decision by the government to abolish the machine-tractor stations and to turn their equipment over to individual collective farms. For a description of earlier changes, see Gregory Bienstock, Solomon M. Schwarz and Aaron Yugow, *Management in Russian Industry and Agriculture*, Oxford University Press, New York, 1944.

2. ECE/FAO, *European Agriculture — A Statement of Problems*, Geneva, 1954, pp. 50 and 55.

wheat in Switzerland at about $4 per bushel, when good Canadian wheat could be imported for about half that amount; or the ludicrous situation of Britain's dumping on the international market in 1957 some 100 million eggs (while importing even more), produced under a subsidy which probably accounted for all of the producers' net income derived from the sale of the eggs.

These are examples (typical of many which could be cited for other commodities and other countries) of rather gross mismanagement by someone. Who is it?

WHO MANAGES AGRICULTURE?

Briefly, the answer to the question is: governments. Despite its place in the classical economics textbooks as the truest example of the free competitive industry, nowhere in the North Atlantic region is agriculture free or competitive. Nearly everywhere its market is rigged — directly by governments or by government-sponsored producers' associations. Nearly everywhere its output is influenced or directed, through financial inducement or threat or edict, by governments. Almost everywhere its marketing processes are interfered with by governments far beyond the requirements of "the public welfare."

Nowhere is there any prospect that this situation will be reversed. No government — not even that of the United Kingdom, where only about one out of every twenty persons of voting age is associated directly with agriculture — can be expected to let farming become a truly competitive industry.

Indeed, it can properly be argued that relinquishment of direction of agriculture by governments would be a seriously irresponsible act. For all its employment of scientific knowledge, its large-scale capital investment and its commercial orientation, farming cannot be called a "modern" business in one very important sense. Unlike any other important economic undertaking in modern societies, undirected agriculture cannot adjust rapidly to changes in the market by large-scale changes in output. In part this is due to the long production cycle. For a period of at least a year the impact of a change in demand must be borne by price changes, not by increases or decreases in output. In part inability to respond quickly arises from the nearly unique position of the farm operator as both capitalist and laborer. On many millions of farms a decision by the farmer as a capitalist to reduce his output would be a decision by the same farmer as a laborer to reduce his employment.

There are two important reasons — both arising from the suddenness with which the new technology of farming struck — why governments will continue to intervene in the management of agriculture. The first is sociological. As indicated in the opening pages of this volume, there are too many farmers still on the land to permit full employment, if they are farming in a modern manner. This will remain so for some time to come, even if governments follow wise policies and the rate of technological change slows (though there is little indication that the latter will occur). No government of a democratic country can afford to allow the "natural laws of the market" to operate in making the necessary adjustment in the number of farmers — their very number guarantees that governments will be responsive to their demands.

The second reason for continued government intervention in agriculture is closely related to the first. In the attempts made to maintain politically satisfactory levels of income for the excessive number of farmers remaining on the land, governments have utilized techniques which have induced a great expansion in output. This development, accompanied by only a modest expansion in demand, has resulted in a growing prevalence of "surpluses" — supplies which the market will not accept at prices deemed high enough to provide satisfactory incomes to growers.

A BRIEF LOOK AT THE PAST

With very few notable exceptions, governments of the nations in the North Atlantic region did not have agricultural policies which went beyond protection of the domestic market until the economic depression of the 1930s. Great Britain, dominant as an industrial producer and international trader, discarded agricultural protection in 1846 and opened the world's richest market to international competition. First the United States and Canada and then Russia, Australia and Argentina responded by supplying large amounts of grain to pay for their imports of British manufactures. In Western Europe Denmark and the Netherlands, severely short of economic resources apart from their land and their people, organized themselves to supply the British market with livestock products. Both, but particularly Denmark, had affirmative farm policies aimed at improving the efficiency of agriculture to make that industry the basis of their international trade.

Figure 2–1. Number of Farms and Land in Farms in the United States, 1850–1959

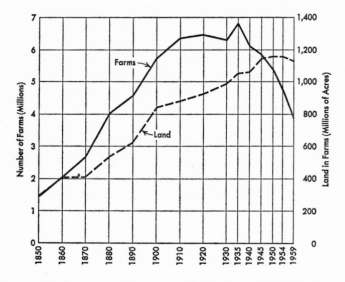

Sources: USDA, *Agricultural Statistics, 1960,* Washington, 1961; U. S. Bureau of the Census, *Census of Agriculture, 1959: Preliminary,* Series AC-59-1, Washington, 1961. 1959 figures adjusted to conform to 1954 census definition.

In the United States and Canada agricultural policies until the 1920s were centered in general foreign trade policies, expansion of farm land and education. Both countries were large-scale grain exporters and the United States was the world's major supplier of cotton and tobacco. Population in the United States and (later) Canada was growing rapidly until World War I and there were great areas of unutilized land. With the British market completely open and agriculture in many of the continental countries generally inefficient, a large and growing domestic and foreign market appeared to be a permanent feature of North American agriculture.

Looking back, one can see that the seeming permanence of an expanding market in Europe after the turn of the century was illusory. Lower birth rates and a high rate of emigration were slowing the growth of population in most European countries. Gradual improvements in European agriculture began slowly to chip away at the volume of imports of food.

The tremendous disruption of European agriculture caused by World War I renewed the demand for imports. The reasonably rapid recovery of European agriculture after the war was to a considerable extent disguised as far as the transatlantic suppliers were concerned, for it coincided with the virtual disappearance of Russia from the international grain market.[3] Soviet exports of cereals throughout the 1920s totaled less than in the single year 1913. Thus, while the main trading countries' total cereals exports (most of which were directed to Western Europe) increased by about a third between the immediate prewar period and the 1920s, the four overseas exporters more than doubled their sales. The illusion of a sustained rate of growth for imports in Europe was fostered in the Western countries.

The United States: Depression and Intervention

Agriculture in the United States in the 1920s, after the sharp adjustment in the immediate postwar years, was in the doldrums. The United States participated much less than other exporters in the absorption of the Soviet share of the grain trade. At home the rate of population growth declined, per capita food consumption was virtually stable and farm prices — much lower than in the 1917–1920 period — remained nearly unchanged until the end of

3. Russian exports of cereals grew rapidly over the first decade of the nineteenth century, and in the years 1909–1911 exceeded the combined exports of the United States, Canada, Australia and Argentina. Ingvar Svennilson, *Growth and Stagnation in the European Economy,* ECE, Geneva, 1954, p. 246.

the decade. Employment opportunities outside farming were not good enough to entice large numbers from the land and there were nearly as many farms and farmers at the end of the decade as at the beginning. Farm incomes ceased to rise after the middle of the decade. Despite considerable pressure, successive Congresses and administrations turned down legislation proposing affirmative government policies for income supports for farmers, notably the Mc-Nary-Haugen bill, which would have raised domestic prices for basic commodities and dumped surpluses abroad at lower prices.

American agriculture entered the depression of the 1930s with only the Federal Farm Board as a general defense for farm income. Legislation establishing this board, passed in 1929, was not designed to meet a decline in demand of the magnitude of the early 1930s. Not until 1933, with the passage of the Agricultural Adjustment Act and the formation of the Commodity Credit Corporation, did the American government effectively undertake policies designed to raise farm incomes.

There is no need to review here the multitude of programs undertaken by the government from 1933 onward, as the policy of specific intervention in the management of agriculture developed.[4] All that is required is to note the very limited success of the policies adopted in meeting the agricultural problem (though the record is not much worse than that in nonagricultural sectors of the economy). Decline in farm income set in again in 1938 and continued through 1940. A sharp recovery in demand and prices in 1941 finally lifted farm incomes back to their predepression level.

Europe between the Wars

Farming in most of Europe stumbled through the greater part of the interwar years without making substantial changes in techniques and without increasing production very much. With most of the countries in over-all deficit positions with respect to food supplies, efforts to protect farm prices by control of imports were simple to undertake. But only in the last years before the outbreak of World

4. These programs have been described with great clarity in two publications of the Twentieth Century Fund by Murray R. Benedict: *Farm Policies of the United States, 1790–1950,* 1953; and *Can We Solve the Farm Problem?,* 1955.

War II did the protected status of agriculture in most European countries give impetus to additional output sufficient to cut sharply into the needs for imports.

Agriculture is the outstanding example of the new policy of national welfare. In no other part of the European economy was the production of one section of the community at the expense of the rest of the nation carried so far. The farming community had suffered severely, first from the direct effects of the war [World War I] and subsequently from the world economic crisis. The various national policies of agricultural protection were designed to mitigate the most catastrophic effects of this crisis, but they could not prevent agriculture in most European countries from showing many of the symptoms of a "depressed industry": low wages, low farm profits, a slow rise in output and productivity and a wasteful use of manpower.

. . . The improvement in productivity in order to make domestic agriculture more competitive was thus usually neglected. On the contrary, the new protective measures often had the effect of preserving an inefficient structure of national agriculture, or of developing it in a way that went contrary to favourable regional and international specialization.

. . . incomes were often maintained above a minimum level even on those farms which, as a result of varying natural conditions for farming or as a result of far-reaching parcellization, could be regarded as of marginal efficiency. . . . To the extent that such great natural differences were neutralized by agricultural policy, it also counteracted the elimination of the least efficient units, or prevented a regional specialization which otherwise would have offered economic advantages.

. . . In no other field was economic nationalism such a striking success to the detriment of general European efficiency. Yet in no other field of comparable importance to Europe as a whole were natural conditions so different and the potential advantages of trade over national frontiers so great; . . .

From a productivity point of view, the protection of agriculture before the war [World War II] thus suffered from a double weakness. On the one hand, it was never able to restore the prosperity of the farmer to a level which would have given a stimulus to rapid modernization. On the other hand, it prevented — by maintaining incomes derived from less efficient production — an increase in productivity through elimination or regional specialization.[5]

5. Ingvar Svennilson, *Growth and Stagnation in the European Economy*, ECE, Geneva, 1954, pp. 88–90.

Such is the evaluation of a protected but not managed agricultural industry in Europe in the late 1930s. It applies, with varying degrees of precision, to agriculture in every country in Western Europe.

THE POSTWAR SITUATION: EUROPE

Western Europe emerged from World War II with an agricultural industry which was fundamentally inefficient. It was underequipped and overmanned — though of the large numbers engaged in farming a disproportionately large share consisted of the old and the very young. Fertilizers, which the best of Europe's agriculture had come to depend on for high yields, were difficult to obtain. Marketing systems had been disrupted on the Continent, where every country except the neutrals had been occupied or defeated by its adversaries.

Europe — the whole area west of the Soviet Union — had three very poor cereals crops in the years 1945, 1946 and 1947.[6] Production of the five main cereals averaged only 76 million tons annually, about three quarters of the annual production during the war years 1940–1944. Exports of cereals, mainly under a system of international allocation, from the four large non-European surplus-producing countries — the United States, Canada, Australia and Argentina — rose to more than 30 million tons in 1947 and 1948, about 50 per cent more than in the years just preceding the war.

The war had moved governments in Europe from mere protection of agriculture to more direct management. In the United Kingdom, the only European belligerent which avoided both defeat and enemy occupation, wartime direction of agricultural activities by the government was detailed. Crop plans were dovetailed with prospective imports, which were themselves planned by an international Combined Food Board sitting in Washington. Slaughtering was closely regulated. Manpower — and womanpower as well, in

6. Svennilson, *op. cit.* Estimates of agricultural production during the war years and through 1946 are somewhat unreliable for a number of countries. However, those for cereals are probably close enough to the facts to be indicative of the general agricultural situation. There is little question that livestock output degenerated more sharply in the final years of the war and the years immediately following than did crop production.

the form of the Women's Land Army — was allocated by official bodies. Marketing arrangements were supervised for virtually every agricultural product.

In Sweden and Switzerland, neutrals in the war but seriously involved in the sense of being deprived of much of their supply from abroad, government intervention was nearly as great as in Britain. The Swiss increased land in crops by more than a quarter during the war, and the government controlled production plans and the marketing of farm output in an effort to make good a large part of the gap in supplies normally met by imports.

In the countries under German control farm production was organized by various means, direct and indirect, in part to provide Germany with needed foodstuffs. Sugar-beet area, for example, was expanded sharply in a number of occupied countries.

The habits and institutions of wartime and the poor crops of the immediate postwar period led almost everywhere to continued government intervention in agriculture. Methods varied from country to country, but in general governments offered inducement prices for desired products, put ceiling prices on some products by monopolizing — or trying to monopolize — the marketing process, encouraged farm organizations through which government objectives could be made known and put into force, offered financial assistance of various sorts to individuals and groups of farmers willing to "cooperate" with government proposals.

There were two immediate motivations for European governments to continue and to extend detailed intervention in agriculture after the war. The first, mentioned above, was the series of poor harvests from 1945 to 1947. The second was the growing realization during these years that nearly every country in Europe was faced with a balance-of-payments problem which was not going to be solved quickly or easily. Every government, as it faced the ever-mounting problem of meeting its import bills, saw an opportunity to reduce those bills by producing more of the country's agricultural requirements.

There were, in addition, more fundamental forces at work at this time to influence governments to assume more detailed management of agriculture.

First, this was the dawn of "the age of planning" in Western Europe. National planning of a sort had made an appearance in Europe in the 1930s. Mussolini's and Hitler's regimes had elements of economic planning in them, though of questionable quality and, in part, objectives. Sweden's "middle way" was a widely publicized and more respectable example of the beginnings of national planning. Denmark's less well-known State Marketing Boards effectively planned that country's most important industry, agriculture.

The postwar period, however, with its gigantic demands on limited resources for reconstruction, required that a system of priorities be established almost everywhere, if economic recovery was to be achieved promptly — in some cases before political chaos could set in to create both social and economic upheaval. By June 1947 U. S. Secretary of State George C. Marshall was suggesting to European governments that, if they would come forward with well-organized plans for their economic reconstruction and not mere "shopping lists," the United States would be willing to provide massive financial assistance in helping to carry out those plans.

Clearly agriculture — one of Europe's least efficient industries — had a place in such planning. In little more than a year most of the governments of Western Europe had drawn up detailed plans to expand greatly their agricultural output by 1952 over not only the low 1947 level but over the prewar level as well.[7]

A second fundamental force influencing governments toward more detailed management of agriculture was that farming had been a depressed industry in most European countries in the interwar years, and protection, in the form of tariffs and import quotas, clearly had not been enough to raise farm incomes to levels comparable with urban incomes. Farming in Denmark, the least protectionist but the most government-managed of continental Europe's agricultural industries, was by far the most prosperous in the sense of maintaining a reasonable parity with nonagricultural incomes (though Danish farmers had gone through some hard times in the 1930s). The woes of European agriculture had come under considerable scrutiny in the interwar period and modest beginnings had

7. OEEC, *Interim Report on The European Recovery Programme,* Paris, 1948; also, ECE, *Economic Survey of Europe in 1948,* Geneva, 1949.

been made toward taking some steps needed if European countries were to obtain greater agricultural output behind the protective walls built around the "national farms." The war had interrupted this process, but there were in all countries many proponents of more explicit government assistance to agriculture. In the postwar situation they found themselves with plentiful political support — support emanating from a combination of rural overrepresentation in most national legislatures and governments and central bankers concerned with the balance-of-payments problems which loomed so large.

The plans which governments produced were detailed. They set out specific goals with respect to output of particular products and the means by which the specified amounts of production could be obtained. However, apart from some rather intensive government direction in the United Kingdom, Sweden, Norway, Italy and Switzerland — particularly in the first few years after the war ended — government direction consisted mainly of education and financial lures offered to producers for doing what the government planners thought should be done, and, of course, of protection. In a situation of general deficiency in supply of most products there was little need for more forceful direction of the decisions of individual growers. Moreover, it must be remembered that the physical structure of the average small farm in Europe, especially on the Continent, very seriously limits the range of alternative decisions to be made by the farmer with respect to land use and, in many instances, methods of production. The great majority of farmers in Western Europe are forced into a pattern of labor-intensive production which usually implies vertical organization of their enterprises: intensive utilization of much of their land to produce high yields of feedstuffs to be fed to livestock maintained by the individual farmer.

The typical pattern of government direction of agriculture in Western Europe involves tariffs, quantitative import restrictions, government-guaranteed minimum prices to be paid by government-authorized purchasers, subsidies for selected items required by growers, financial assistance at preferred terms for making specified farm improvements and organization of marketing mechanisms (some of which are the vehicles for maintaining minimum prices).

This sort of direction of agriculture is clearly best suited to nations whose domestic production is not sufficient to meet demand at the price levels established by governments. In this circumstance the key implement is the import quota, which can be denied until assurance is had that the domestic supply will clear the market at the established price. The government is relieved of the necessity for propping up the market prices by direct financial action, passing that expense to the ultimate consumer. In general this has been possible for most commodities in the majority of European countries in the years since the war.

Protection of agriculture at the frontier is a much less effective device for those commodities which are produced in surplus quantities in relation to domestic demand. Denmark and the Netherlands, as major exporting countries of livestock products, until recently depended to a considerable extent on maintaining domestic prices for their export products at the same levels as their foreign sale prices. (The situation in the Netherlands was not quite so "pure" as that in Denmark, due to the imposition of an import levy on feedstuffs and a subsequent "drawback" of the levy by exporters of livestock products.)

France has for long had surpluses of various crops coupled with high government-supported prices paid to producers, and has acted to meet the problem in myriad ways. Excess output of wheat, sugar beets and wine has been used to produce industrial alcohol which the government then sold at a loss. Export subsidies have been paid on these products. Special contractual arrangements for exports, which lessened the subsidies, have been made in some cases. Despite such efforts, French agricultural policies have frequently aroused dissatisfaction, particularly among milk producers and growers of potatoes and vegetables, as well as among the producers of the crops mentioned above.

Italy has developed a surplus of soft wheat, which has been disposed of only by export subsidies. The same is true of Sweden, despite government efforts to restrict production. Many countries have milk and egg surpluses.

Generally speaking, protection of agriculture at the frontier is progressively becoming less effective as a method of farm support, as production of various products in more European countries exceeds domestic requirements at the guaranteed prices. It is this trend which raises questions as to the efficacy of the Common Market's agricultural policy described in the preceding chapter. Its great dependence on isolating the European market from external competition would surely make it no more than a temporary palliative, unless the United Kingdom is included within its borders. This becomes clear in the analysis later in this volume concerning output and consumption prospects.

Even with the supplying of the United Kingdom's deficiencies in output reserved to continental producers, the problems of European agriculture will come to resemble more and more those of North America. Their solution must be found in basic policies aimed at "restructuring" agriculture — the sort of policies which the United States, where the nature of the problem has been clearer for a longer period of time, has been so conspicuously unable to adopt.

Before we turn to a review of efforts and techniques used primarily to improve farm incomes in recent years, it is necessary to take a brief glance at two other factors which were important in bringing European agriculture in the postwar period into its present shape.

The Balance of Payments

The national economies of Western Europe, with few exceptions, were faced with serious problems in meeting their import bills in the immediate postwar period. While these problems were badly underestimated in the first year or two following the end of fighting, they loomed large by 1947 as a result of several factors: a rapid rise in the prices of raw materials, foodstuffs and many basic industrial products as controls were lifted, particularly in the United States; failure of Europe's basic energy industry — coal — to recover as rapidly as might have been expected; a new appraisal of the extent of need for and cost of reequipping industry and transport, which had not only been badly damaged by warfare but had also become increasingly obsolescent as six years of war followed a decade

— in some places much more than that — of neglect; a radically changed relationship with overseas affiliated areas, leading in some instances to independence but in all cases to conditions of reduced profitability, or even of unprofitability, for the European nations involved.

Thus, what appeared in 1945 and 1946 to be problems solvable by some emergency assistance (primarily through the United Nations Relief and Rehabilitation Administration, about three quarters of whose funds were contributed by the United States) and loans of some $6 billion[8] were seen in 1947 and 1948 to be of much greater magnitude than had been supposed.

Under these circumstances it appeared to most Western European governments that any saving that could be made on the imported food bill was highly desirable, even if the cost of obtaining additional domestic production was high. In general governments acted on that principle, shaping their agricultural programs and subsidies in a manner to put a premium on additional output. Nearly all of them established guaranteed (high) prices for farm products, and myriad subsidies on the items farmers needed to buy in order to obtain greater output. In most countries importation of foodstuffs became virtual monopolies of agencies of the state and rationing and price controls directed demand to the fullest extent possible toward home-produced commodities.

In the narrow context of helping to meet the balance-of-payments problem, the postwar agricultural policies in Western Europe were eminently successful. In 1947/48, when the outlook was darkest with respect to Europe's foreign trade balance, home-produced cereals accounted for 68 per cent of total cereals available, while 32 per cent were imported from non-European markets. By

8. Apart from settlement of lend-lease supplies still in the "pipeline" at the end of the war and miscellaneous settlements, such as surplus property credits, loans by the United States to Western Europe — particularly Britain and France — totaled about $5 billion in the first two years after hostilities were ended. Additionally, Canada extended loans exceeding $1 billion during the same period, mainly to the United Kingdom. See IMF, *Balance of Payments Yearbook, 1938, 1946, 1947*, Washington, 1949, pp. 107, 191, 193, 344, 345, 365 and 366.

1953/54, when it had become safe to be optimistic about foreign trade prospects for most Western European countries, total cereals available had risen by 45 per cent and home production accounted for 86 per cent of the total.[9]

Much the same development took place with other commodities. Domestic sugar accounted for about half the total supplies in Western Europe in 1947/48 and about three quarters in the middle years of the 1950s. Meat imports constituted about 16 per cent of the total consumed in 1947/48 and about 6 per cent a few years later.

Thus Europe's farmers made a substantial contribution to the effort to redress the foreign accounts of most countries in the first decade following the war under the increasing managerial efforts of their governments. The success, however, was not unalloyed. Expanded output came at rather high costs. It must also be remembered that the policies followed were autarkic in the extreme. Virtually no effort was made under the aegis of the Organisation for European Economic Cooperation (OEEC) to take advantage of the possibilities of greater regional specialization within Europe itself. This could have been undertaken without detriment to the effort to overcome the basic balance-of-payments difficulties of the period, which concerned for the most part the relations of Western Europe as a whole with the outside world — particularly the "dollar area." A more concerted effort in agriculture would presumably have resulted in more economic production of output of the same magnitudes. At the same time it would have improved trading relations in nonagricultural goods within Europe, by making more flexible the import control policies of those countries which were in a position to expand their agricultural output if they could but find markets. And this could have been done without increasing the "dollar gap."

9. OEEC, *Agricultural and Food Statistics,* Paris, 1959, p. 78. The comparison is not entirely a fair one, as several countries, notably Denmark, France and Germany, suffered a poor year in 1947, while 1953 was favorable in most countries. Nevertheless, expansion of cereals production in Western Europe has been quite steady since 1947, with only one year — 1954 — failing to show an increase over the preceding year. OEEC, *General Statistics,* Paris, July 1960.

National Security

The reasoning behind the autarkic development in agricultural policy in the individual countries of Western Europe was unquestionably not related solely to the balance-of-payments problem. In every country the argument was heard that a large supply of home-produced foodstuffs was mandatory insurance against disaster in case of war. It was an old argument, of course, strongly buttressed by experiences in both world wars.

From a national standpoint the argument is unquestionably spurious in the politico-military conditions of Western Europe in the postwar period. The political alignments and the techniques of warfare have so changed that national self-sufficiency in food production for the individual countries of Western Europe would not assure a wartime food supply. At least since 1950 there has been explicit agreement among most of the countries of Western Europe (and implicit agreement among the traditional neutrals) that a major war in Europe would be fought against the Soviet Union (and perhaps its satellites, or some of them), with immediate American participation, and that the war would be fought with weapons of a sort which would make a protracted period of warfare unlikely. Moreover, the methods being adopted for agricultural production in the postwar years were not consistent with the concept of a long period of siege or blockade. Supplies of petroleum products for tractors and trucks on farms and for diesel locomotives and barges would be endangered as much as overseas food supplies in the event of a long war. If the national security argument were a serious one, government policies would not have permitted the decimation of the stock of draft animals which has taken place unhindered in every country in Europe.

INCOME SUPPORT FOR FARMING

By the middle of the 1950s the balance-of-payments situation in most countries of Western Europe had improved to the point that it could scarcely be accepted (which did not prevent its continuing to be used, however) as a justification for increasing agricultural output with little regard for efficiency. And throughout the 1950s it was becoming increasingly clear that European agriculture, while increasing its output, was far from being as prosperous as other sectors of the economy.

The emphasis of agricultural policies gradually shifted from increasing output to increasing incomes of farmers. Both elements, of course, had been present in the policies of most countries since at least the 1930s. It is probably fair to say, however, that the balance-of-payments argument in most European countries provided motivation for agricultural expansion equal to that of improved farm incomes during the first several years after the war.

In the United States and Canada the primary motivation for government farm policies was that of improving farm incomes. In both countries profitability of agriculture began to slump in the last years of the 1940s. Checked temporarily by a sharp upturn in demand at the time of the Korean War, weakness again characterized the farm income situation in North America.

Throughout the North Atlantic area governments use the same two approaches, though differing in emphasis, in attacking the problem of farm incomes. The first is the widespread use of price supports, which in many instances go well beyond the protection from foreign competition described above. The second is to encourage the farmer to improve his efficiency — to widen the spread between his costs of production and the (frequently supported) market prices of his output. The intention of both kinds of policies is, say governments, to obtain approximate parity of income for farmers and nonfarmers of comparable skills.[10]

> The general aim of agricultural policy is to secure for Belgian farmers the better living and working conditions enjoyed by other classes of the community. [p. 31.] To achieve a reasonable standard of living for the [German] agricultural population working on well-managed farms, . . . [p. 91.] This policy is dictated by two needs: first, to sustain [Italian] agricultural income, and second, to direct production along lines consonant with the country's economic requirements. [p. 153.] The policy . . . is that [Canadian] producers should be enabled to make a reasonable living by their own efforts once they

10. OEEC, *Agricultural Policies in Europe and North America,* Second Report of the Ministerial Committee for Agriculture and Food, Paris, 1957.

have been shielded from the worst consequences of being left quite unaided. [p. 359.] The price support measures which are an essential part of the United States Government's agricultural programme are designed to stabilize and improve living standards in the agricultural sector. [p. 375.]

Price Supports

By far the most prevalent method of attempting to sustain or raise farm income is through governmental action to maintain prices of agricultural products at specified levels. Every country in the North Atlantic region utilizes this technique for at least some agricultural products. In some countries (e.g., Switzerland, France and Norway) it is used for virtually every important product. In Denmark the government intervenes in this manner only for sugar beets and industrial potatoes (and recently for cereals and skim milk), but cooperative marketing sponsored by the government in effect extends the system to other products (though generally at relatively low price levels). In the United Kingdom the prices of most goods are allowed to fluctuate, but the producer is guaranteed a specified price, which the government makes good, if necessary, by a "deficiency payment" — the difference between the average market price and the specified price. Additionally, various forms of marketing agreements help to stabilize prices. The U. S. government intervenes, by purchases, commodity loans and marketing agreements, to establish support prices for most important products. Canada "organizes the market" and in some cases directly supports prices of cereals, dairy products and (more recently) eggs, pigs and wool.

Systems of administration of price supports differ considerably, but more important are the differences in price levels at which the supports become effective. Table 2–1 indicates the range of average prices farmers received for wheat in selected countries in 1954–1958. Not only is the range very great, but in every country in Europe farmers are paid more, usually for wheat of inferior quality, than the import price.

Intervention to support prices is comparatively difficult for countries with surplus output, as experience in the United States in the

Table 2–1. Average Prices (per Ton) of Domestic and Imported Wheat, by Country, 1954–1958

COUNTRY	DOMESTIC	IMPORTED	DOMESTIC AS PER CENT OF IMPORTED
Canada	$ 61		
U. S.	72		
EEC[a]			
Belgium	92	$69	133
France	83	(73)	(114)
Germany	98	73	134
Italy	113	90	126
Netherlands	71	68	104
EFTA[b]			
Austria	96	80	120
Denmark	82	73	112
Norway	119	75	159
Sweden	80	(75)	103
Switzerland	150	89	169
U. K.	82	74	111

Sources: ECE/FAO, *European Agriculture in 1965,* Geneva, 1961; FAO, *Monthly Bulletin,* Rome, March 1961.

a. Data not available for Luxembourg.
b. Data not available for Portugal.

1930s and again in the 1950s has so vividly demonstrated. By one means or another it is necessary to establish two prices for the same product — a higher price for domestic sales and a lower one for foreign sales. Whether this process is carried out abroad by a universally stigmatized program of "dumping" or a much-lauded program of "food for peace" is to a very great extent a matter of semantics from the standpoint of price-supporting systems. Both, if they are successful, reduce the price-depressing pressure which hangs over a particular market of surpluses.[11]

11. It is true, of course, that the impact of indiscriminate dumping abroad by means of export subsidies can differ from that of selective gifts or underpriced sales to specific markets. Thus the system employed by the United States of subsidizing the sales abroad of grain probably helped to lower the "world market price" to the benefit of normal commercial buyers — mainly

The two actions are virtually identical in the short run in that they shift a part of production into the market at reduced prices. Viewed from the standpoint of other economies, sales of wheat by the United States at prices below those in the domestic market constitute a donation of American resources. For the non-American producer of similar commodities, they are a disruptive form of "unfair competition." The most charitable evaluation of such actions is that they "make the best of a bad job": after having induced farmers, partly by means of price supports, to produce unsalable quantities of specific products, the least objectionable next step is to see that such surpluses are used.

There are several criticisms to be made of direct support of prices as a means of supporting farm incomes. Dual pricing, to which surplus-producing countries must resort if they are to make their price-supporting techniques work, is only the most conspicuous of them.

The most serious defect in most systems of price support is the absence of an accompanying control over the volume of production. Though some effort has been made to limit production in conjunction with the use of price supports, such controls have been really effective in very few instances.

The essence of price support as a means for improving farm incomes is that it provides a margin between production costs and selling prices. Costs of production vary widely within countries as well as between countries. Moreover, in the present state of application of production techniques, the marginal cost — the additional cost of producing additional amounts of output — is more than likely to be well below the average production cost and the support price. On the best-managed farms the marginal cost may well be rising, but in the present state of rapid change in agricultural technology it is probably unusual for a farmer not to be able to make at least some additional profit out of more output. On farms managed less efficiently it is probable that the marginal cost of production is still

---

Europeans — but almost certainly did not contribute much to more sales. "Sales" of wheat to India in exchange for virtually blocked rupees may, at least in the short run, expand consumption in that country above what it would have been in the absence of such a transaction.

falling, so that an increase in output will bring not only more total profit but a better average profit as well.

In these circumstances firm price supports high enough to satisfy a "politically sufficient" proportion of producers can result only in more output, unless accompanied by a rigorous system of production and marketing controls. If the additional output is not desired (which it is not in those countries in demand-supply equilibrium or already producing surpluses at prices above the world market), the effort to improve farm incomes by means of high price supports is likely to prove self-defeating. The consumer may not have been fully aware that he was paying high prices for his purchases. When surpluses become substantial and must be held by the government or disposed of abroad at a loss, the consumer in his role of taxpayer is likely to become acutely aware of what the price-support program is costing him. He will, sooner or later, demand that production be limited or prices be lowered. Either defeats the objective of improving farm incomes.

In countries with a deficiency in domestic output the problem is essentially the same but is somewhat disguised. The question for them is one of deciding whether additional output obtained at high price supports is in fact desirable. For example, is the maintenance of a high support price for wheat in Germany advantageous without production controls, thereby encouraging the displacement of cheap imported wheat by high-priced domestic wheat? Or would it be better to limit domestic wheat output supported at high prices and continue to import cheap wheat? The more economic answer is in no doubt; unhappily, the politics of agriculture in Germany and elsewhere has been such that the economic answer is nearly irrelevant.

Paying $3 a bushel for German wheat and thus evoking a greater supply when a better quality of wheat can be bought abroad for two thirds that price is an "economic sin." Unfortunately, it is difficult in a political arena to find a voice prepared to be raised against this form of sin. It is easier to point out that German farmers too must live.

A second problem of some consequence raised by specific commodity price supports is that of distortion of consumer choice and responses. It can hardly be questioned that the maintenance of high milk prices, while contributing to growing surpluses of milk, has been a major factor in the substitution of vegetable fats for butter and probably has been partially responsible for the limited growth of demand for both fluid milk and cheese in many countries. In all probability high feed grain prices in many European countries have been partly the cause of relatively modest consumption of pork, poultry and eggs.

Specific price supports tend to tempt farmers into making very dubious investments in capital equipment. While it is probably true, as indicated above, that most farmers are not producing as much as would maximize their profits under fixed prices, there are certainly some who — if there were any substantial risk with respect to prices they hope to receive — would be dissuaded from increasing their expenditures on equipment, particularly of a very specialized sort.

Finally, a serious criticism of price supports can be made on the ground that it is virtually impossible to determine what they actually cost. The longer a price-support system has been in operation the more difficult it is to judge what responses from producers a lower price level would evoke. It is thus very difficult to make a reasonable judgment as to the contribution of price supports to agricultural incomes.

Deficiency Payments

A somewhat different system of price support from that usually employed is used in the United Kingdom (and, to less extent, in other countries). Briefly, the British government does not attempt to establish the market price for most agricultural products (though it does influence the price level by application of tariffs and certain kinds of import restrictions on some commodities). The market is free to fluctuate on the basis of the supplies (including imports) offered and the prices offered. What the government does undertake to do for the home producer is to make up the difference between what he actually received (on the average) for his output and what he would have received had the market price been equal to a specified level. The methods of administration of this "deficiency payment" vary greatly from commodity to commodity, but their effect is the same.

Exaggerated claims of the superiority of the deficiency payment over direct market-price support have sometimes been made. In practice the former has exhibited many of the defects of the more commonly used techniques. Nevertheless, it has some desirable attributes which might be worthy of consideration in the context of a modified common agricultural policy in the EEC and revisions of American policies.

The deficiency-payment system has the economic advantage (and the political disadvantage) of being analyzable with respect to cost.[12] With the market prices competitively established and the funds used to make the deficiency payments appropriated by the legislature, the fog which covers the true costs of direct market-price supports is to a very considerable degree lifted.

What this means in practice is that, as the spread between the market price and the farmer's guaranteed price for particular commodities shows unusual widening or narrowing, the course of proper corrective action by the government can be seen rather clearly. Under the present British system the guaranteed prices can be reduced (after taking into account changes in production costs) by 2.5 per cent annually for all commodities taken together. However, for any specific commodity the reduction may be as much as 4 per cent. There is thus opportunity for correcting specific guaranteed prices in a manner to keep them roughly parallel with the pattern of relative market prices. To the extent this corrective action is taken, the price-deficiency payment resembles to a considerable degree an income subsidy for farmers regardless of the commodity being produced.

Income support for farmers while they pass through an extraordinary period of technological upheaval is the main objective of governments. Market-price support for commodities is a means to this end — a rather poor one, it must be admitted. A well-administered system of deficiency payments has a chance to succeed in distributing government support to farmers without warping beyond the point of repair price relations of various commodities. It at least keeps in touch with the world market situation with respect to in-

12. This overstates the case to the extent that tariffs and other barriers distort the market prices from which the amount of the deficiency payment is calculated. In the British situation these distortions are relatively minor.

dividual commodities, and in that respect is infinitely superior to a system of specific price supports determined in a situation in which international prices have been so isolated as to be barred from effective consideration.

Closely related to this advantage of the deficiency payment over market-price support is that of restoration of a degree of "sovereignty of the consumer." With market prices for various commodities freely established, the consumer is free to exercise his choice of products in a much more meaningful way under the deficiency-payment system than under the market-price-support mechanism. The consumer has proved himself to be rather adroit in adjusting his buying habits to an imperfectly administered system of market-price supports. His selectivity in buying, however, takes place in a market which is quite irregularly rigged. No one really knows how much butter and how much margarine and vegetable oils the American consumer would have bought if milk and oilseeds had been sold in a free market over the past ten years, with the producers of both receiving deficiency payments rather than unequally matched market-price supports.

Perhaps not too much should be made of these economic advantages of the deficiency-payment system of price support. The system still must be supplemented by some kind of output controls, as the British have learned in regard to milk, eggs and potatoes. Moreover, in a major exporting country, such as Canada or the United States, it would probably be necessary to make some considerable adjustments in the system for the main commodities sold abroad.

Nevertheless, if the problems of agriculture are to be faced in a rational manner, it would be of great help to be able to establish with a considerable degree of accuracy the real costs of price supports — not only the costs borne by government treasuries but also those borne by consumers buying in markets insulated from foreign supplies available at lower prices. A gradual shift from direct market-price supports to deficiency payments might well provide a useful modification of the EEC's common agricultural policy as well as of the policies of the United States.

The Cost of Price Supports

From what has been said above it is clear that the total cost of price supports to the public is far more than direct government outlays for such purposes. Indeed, seven of fourteen[13] countries of the North Atlantic region could claim that in 1955 direct government outlays for price supports were nil or almost negligible. These seven countries were engaged in efforts to support farm prices; they simply were using, in the main, extrabudgetary means for achieving their objectives. Elsewhere, because such extrabudgetary means were not easily applicable to the problem or because support operations were made from budgeted funds as deficiency payments, government expenditures were substantial. In absolute terms expenditures of public funds for prices received by farmers were highest in the United States — over $1.3 billion; on a per capita basis they were highest in the United Kingdom (Table 2–2).

The extrabudgetary cost of price-support operations — the gap between the actual market price as maintained by government actions and the hypothetical price which would have obtained in the absence of those actions — is, of course, the major factor in determining the total effect of price supports on farm income. Measuring that gap is an exercise in what might be called "metaeconomics" which will not be attempted at this point. One hypothetical example is perhaps sufficient to demonstrate the importance of the point.

It is probably safe to say that over the past few years in a North Atlantic market unhampered by trade restrictions a price structure for cereals permitting wheat to be delivered to European ports at $75 per ton would have elicited an almost unlimited supply from North America. Actual prices have been roughly $70 per ton.

North American wheat at $75 per ton in European ports would be competitive with European wheat priced (for the farmer) at something like $55 to $60 per ton (the price ranging according to inland transport costs and quality differentials). Since 1957 only in Denmark and the United Kingdom has the wheat price

13. The analysis here excludes Portugal, for which comparable data are not available. See Table 2–2.

Table 2–2. Government Expenditures in Direct Support of Agricultural Prices Received by Producers, 1955

COUNTRY	TOTAL, MILLIONS	PER CAPITA	AS PER CENT OF AVERAGE NET INCOME OF FARM OPERATORS[a]
Canada	$ 8	$0.50	0.5
U. S.	1,350	8.10	10.7
EEC			
BLEU	2	0.20	0.4
France	133	3.10	(3.8)
Germany	7	0.15	0.3
Italy	6	0.12	0.2
Netherlands	31	2.80	5.4
EFTA[b]			
Austria	—	—	—
Denmark	—	—	—
Norway	5	1.50	3.0
Sweden	39	5.40	11.3
Switzerland[c]	21	4.20	(6.4)
U. K.	441	8.60	(34.9)

Sources: Derived from OEEC, *Agricultural Policies,* Second Report, Paris, 1957; Appendix I, Table A; and sources shown in Appendix II, text (for Table B).
  a. Before allowance for rent and interest.
  b. Data not available for Portugal.   c. 1954.

been under $75. In Switzerland the price has been as much as $150, in Italy about $110, in Germany over $100, in Belgium over $90. None of these countries uses public funds of any consequence in support of wheat prices. They merely restrain, by various means, import of wheat (and other products) which would depress the domestic wheat price below selected levels.

By forcing millers to pay these prices for domestic wheat, rather than purchasing wheat available from abroad at lower prices, governments in these countries divert substantial amounts of income to farmers. Thus in Germany, where about 5 million tons of bread grains are marketed each year, growers receive some $225 million more than they would otherwise obtain. In Italy the comparable figure is perhaps $400 million per year, in Switzerland $25 million and in Belgium-Luxembourg about $20 million.[14]

This special pricing for domestic output extends to other products, of course, particularly to almost all the important food products entering into international trade — feed grains, meat, eggs, various milk products and sugar — if there is a deficit in domestic supply or if the governments can contrive means for withholding supplies from the market.

Thus the $1.3 billion spent by the United States government in 1955 in direct support of market prices for agricultural products was not the full "subsidy" enjoyed by American farmers. Direct price supports were not required for sugar, for example, for which the domestic price to farmers was well in excess of the prevailing prices in the main cane-producing areas. By pushing up the price (through tariffs and special contractual arrangements) at which foreign-produced raw sugar could enter the American market the American government assured farmers of a higher price for sugar beets than they could otherwise have obtained — and assured them a market, as well, without resort to direct governmental subsidy. The subsidy was paid by the consumer in the market price of sugar.

As indicated above, estimating the full cost of price supports rivals in difficulty determining the number of angels able to stand on the head of a pin. Perhaps the best estimate is possible for the United Kingdom, where the system of deficiency payments is most widely used. In 1958/59 total net income (after depreciation) from farming was estimated at £315.5 million ($883 million). Of this amount, nearly half — £155 million — came from the government in the form of deficiency payments.[15]

---

14. It should be understood that these "subsidies" are calculated against a hypothetical price for imported wheat of $75 per ton, a price which is substantially higher than that prevailing until recently. If the countries in Western Europe should decide progressively to permit free or fixed-duty entry of wheat, the general market price would probably not be affected to the extent of raising the cost of wheat landed at European ports above this amount.

15. *Annual Review and Determination of Guarantees, 1960,* HMSO, London, 1960. The £155 million in deficiency payments includes costs of administration — perhaps £3 million. However, it excludes some £80 mil-

To this would have to be added some unknown amount to cover costs to consumers resulting from tariffs (which are, however, generally low) and from seasonal import quota restrictions, which tend to hold the market price of certain commodities above the level at which those commodities could be obtained from abroad. The amount would probably not be large.

The £155 million of deficiency payments represented over 10 per cent of the value of farm marketings in Britain in that year (including the deficiency payments themselves). From this it might be deduced that market-price-supporting operations contribute about the same percentage of the value of farm marketings in other countries with approximately the same price levels as in Britain.[16]

Table 2–3 gives a very rough approximation of what the cost of a deficiency-payment system would have been for cereals in the late years of the 1950s had it been in use in European countries in place of the complex of protective devices actually employed. Except for Britain, for which actual payments are used, the values are estimates relating the prices actually received by farmers (applied to total production, whether marketed or used on the farm) to the average prices paid for imported cereals. The fact that no account is taken of quality differentials (except for the United Kingdom and for wheat for France and Sweden) tends to narrow the spread between import prices and domestic prices and thus tends to understate the hypothetical value of deficiency payments. The estimates are also based on the assumption that the cost of delivering imported wheat to the mill and feed grains to the farm is equal to the cost of delivering domestic cereals to the point of final use.

Very roughly, this is the hidden "tax bill" paid by the consumer in the prices ultimately charged for cereals products and livestock products produced from domestic grain (except in the United King-

---

lion of various other subsidies for agriculture, the most important of which — £36 million for fertilizers and lime — was scarcely distinguishable in its effect from a price subsidy for crops.

16. This generalization would have to be modified somewhat for some countries, e.g., Austria and Switzerland, where access to imported commodities could be had only at somewhat higher prices, owing to transport costs, than those prevailing in the United Kingdom.

Table 2–3. Rough Estimate of the Hypothetical Costs of Deficiency Payments as a Means of Price Support for Cereals, by European Country, Late 1950s

	HYPOTHETICAL VALUE OF PAYMENTS, MILLIONS		VALUE OF HYPOTHETICAL PAYMENTS AS PER CENT OF TOTAL VALUE OF PRODUCTION	
COUNTRY	BREAD GRAINS	COARSE GRAINS	BREAD GRAINS	COARSE GRAINS
EEC				
BLEU	$ 26	$ 4	28	8
France	140	—	20	—
Germany	204	153	29	31
Italy	260	89	31	26
Netherlands	7	8	12	13
EFTA				
Austria	17	—	18	—
Denmark	1	20	2	8
Norway	1	5	38	6
Portugal	27	3	31	12
Sweden	16	11	19	6
Switzerland	25	8	46	46
U. K.	54[a]	93[a]	24	20

Sources: Except for the United Kingdom, calculations are based on the difference between average import prices (export prices for France and Sweden) and average prices paid to producers, as given in ECE, *Economic Survey of Europe in 1960,* Geneva, 1961, Chap. 3. These values were multiplied by average annual production for 1956–1959 as given in OEEC, *General Statistics,* Paris, May 1961.

The values for the United Kingdom are actual deficiency payments in 1958/59 as given in HMSO, *Annual Review and Determination of Guarantees, 1960,* London, 1960.

dom, where deficiency payments were actually paid and were thus not hidden, though a tariff on some feed grains was). The same sort of spread between import prices and domestic prices of meat also prevails in most countries, reflecting to a considerable extent the use of high-cost feedstuffs.

The Economic Commission for Europe (whose work forms the basis for the estimates made here) has attempted a rough estimate of the degree of protection afforded by most European countries to their own producers for the most important products. This estimate is reproduced (in a different form) in Table 2–4. The countries are ranked under each commodity heading according to the extent of protection (the percentage by which import prices fall below domestic prices, after adjustment for quality differences in most cases). It can be seen from these arrays that Denmark stands out as the only country which had, in the latter part of the 1950s, competitive prices for virtually all commodities. The Netherlands stands well with respect to livestock products, but cereals are highly protected. French domestic and import prices seem fairly competitive, but part of this good showing is probably due to the exchange rate used to make the comparison.[17] For most countries and most commodities, except milk and eggs, there is a considerable concentration of national protective rates in the range of about 15 to 30 per cent. Switzerland, however, appears as a very highly protected market for all items.

OTHER AGRICULTURAL SUBSIDIES

Price supports, direct or indirect, are not the only subsidies received by agriculture. From the standpoint of any but the most extreme of free-market–oriented economists, many such subsidies are desirable and some of them should surely be extended. A few verge on the preposterous, viewed economically.

Many of these subsidies are designed to do for farmers what farmers cannot easily do for themselves. Nearly all of them are designed to raise farm output per worker or per unit of land area or both, with the intention — or hope — that such increased output will make farming more profitable and less dependent on price-support actions.

Research and Education

The most fundamental of such subsidies is that for research and experimentation in agriculture and dissemination of the results to

17. The French franc was devalued by some 17 per cent in December 1958 and the new rate was applied to domestic prices and import prices for the years 1958/59 and 1959/60 in making these calculations. There have been strong pressures (which have met with some success) for upward revisions of agricultural prices since then.

Table 2–4. Rough Estimate of the Degree of Protection[a] for Major Agricultural Commodities, Selected European Countries, Late 1950s

DEGREE OF PROTECTION (PER CENT)[a]	COMMODITY, BY COUNTRY						
	WHEAT	BARLEY	SUGAR	BEEF	PORK	MILK	EGGS
0–10		Denmark Austria France	France Netherlands Denmark	Denmark Portugal	Denmark Belgium Netherlands Portugal	Denmark	Denmark Netherlands France Austria
11–20	Denmark France	Belgium Portugal Sweden Norway	Austria	Austria France	Norway Austria		Norway
21–30	U.K. Netherlands Sweden Austria	Netherlands U.K.	Belgium Sweden Italy U.K.	Belgium U.K. Norway Germany Italy Sweden Netherlands	Italy Germany U.K.		Sweden U.K.

Continued on following page

Table 2–4 (continued)

DEGREE OF PROTECTION (PER CENT)[a]	COMMODITY, BY COUNTRY						
	WHEAT	BARLEY	SUGAR	BEEF	PORK	MILK	EGGS
31–40	Germany Portugal Belgium Italy	Italy Germany	Germany Switzerland	Switzerland	Switzerland	Netherlands France Austria Germany	Italy Germany
41–50	Norway					Switzerland	Switzerland
Over 50	Switzerland	Switzerland				Italy Norway U.K.	

Source: ECE, *Economic Survey of Europe in 1960,* Geneva, 1961, Chap. 3.

a. The percentage by which a significant European import — occasionally export — price falls below prices paid to domestic producers, after adjustment for quality differences for some commodities.

the agricultural population. While producers' associations, particularly in Scandinavia, finance much of this sort of assistance to individual farmers, governments throughout the region are heavily engaged in improving the technical knowledge available to the farm population.

In the United States extensive research in both technical and economic aspects of agriculture is undertaken by state universities and colleges, as well as by government experiment stations and laboratories. In general they work closely with various bureaus of the U. S. Department of Agriculture. Applicable results of such efforts are spread among farmers through the U. S. Extension Service and comparable state-financed agencies and through government cooperation with producers' organizations. Supplementing these publicly financed efforts, of course, are the educational activities carried on by producers of farm equipment and supplies — activities which cannot be considered subsidies to agriculture, but which would be of much less importance in the absence of the subsidized research carried on by public agencies.

In Canada a similar government program exists to bring technical assistance to farming. Throughout Scandinavia and in the Netherlands great effort has been made for many decades in the field of research and education in agriculture. About a third of all government expenditure for agriculture in Denmark went for these purposes in the 1950s. Some thirty agricultural schools received state assistance.

In Germany and Switzerland substantial government expenditures, by federal as well as *Länder* and cantonal agencies, are devoted to agricultural education and research. In recent years these programs have been expanded greatly in the United Kingdom. France and Italy, which generally spend relatively small amounts for these purposes, in recent years have attempted to direct their research toward the pressing regional problems in the south of both countries.

Environmental Subsidies

Expenditures by governments for programs for land improvement and control of pests and diseases are greater than are expenditures for agricultural education and research in most countries.

Table 2–5. Government Expenditures for Selected Objectives, Other than Price Support, in Agriculture, by Country, Mid–1950s

COUNTRY	RESEARCH, EDUCATION AND CREDIT[a]	ENVIRON-MENTAL IMPROVE-MENTS[b]	MEANS OF PRODUC-TION[c]	MARKET-ING AND OTHER[d]
Canada	$50	$ 1,100	$ (550)	$1,430
U. S.[e]	26	1,000	—	250
EEC				
BLEU	34	1,400	780	1,080
France	4	2,200	5,040	490
Germany	11	9,400	1,100	1,230
Italy	3	12,000	810	1,320
Netherlands	35	22,000	260	—
EFTA				
Austria	9	4,600	9,170	440
Denmark	12	2,000	110	—
Norway	40	8,600	25,390	670
Sweden	29	2,200	2,160	2,600
Switzerland	34	13,600	. . .	. . .
U. K.	29	2,900	8,280	3,840

Sources: OEEC, *Agricultural Policies,* Second Report, Paris, 1957; and Appendix II, Tables A–D.
   a. Per man-year of labor input.
   b. Per 1,000 hectares of agricultural land.
   c. Per $100,000 of current purchases by farm operators.
   d. Per $100,000 of agricultural output.   e. Federal expenditures only.

In the Netherlands, where these expenditures are highest in relation to both population and cultivated land, reclamation work is very largely a public responsibility. The situation is somewhat similar in Germany and Switzerland, as well as in Italy, where major land improvement programs are being carried out, particularly in the southern part of the country. In all these countries (and in Norway) expenditures for these purposes are high.

Elsewhere in Europe and in North America governmental expenditures for these purposes in the mid–1950s were much more modest, running from about $1 to $5 per hectare (Table 2–5).

Subsidizing Inputs and Marketing

In nearly every country in the region in the mid–1950s subsidies were granted to farmers to permit them to buy under the market price various production requisites. In several countries storage facilities were subsidized and in a few there were special transportation subsidies granted to assist in marketing farm products. Only in Denmark, the Netherlands and the United States were expenditures for such purposes of minor importance.[18] Germany and Italy both subsidized their farmers to a considerable amount by provision of storage below cost, while Canada and Switzerland granted important transportation subsidies.

With regard to the subsidization of agricultural inputs a number of countries made fertilizers available below cost. Some subsidized cereal and other feeds and many directly subsidized tractor fuels and/or freed them from taxes. In France farmers received a subsidy of 15 per cent of the cost of agricultural equipment.

This is far from a complete list of the benefits conferred on agriculture by governments. Intergovernmental committees working under the aegis of the OEEC have made comprehensive studies which give in detail the many and varied means by which governments have taken over much of the work of bringing the farmer into line with his industrial counterpart with respect to controlled marketing, research, access to finance, investment and myriad other aspects of a modern industrial world.

Government intervention in the management of agriculture has been eminently successful from the standpoint of raising output, though, as discussed later, it has not been nearly so successful in improving farm incomes. Its proven ability to increase production has resulted in a situation in which the output of the region has progressively outstripped the growth of demand. The governments of the countries of the North Atlantic region, autarkical in their agricultural policies, have set the stage on which a new and difficult international agricultural conflict has already begun to appear.

18. The payment by the U. S. government to farmers for on-farm storage of commodities owned or held under loan by the Commodity Credit Corporation is not classed as a subsidy in the estimate shown in Table 2–5.

CHAPTER

3

Land and Labor

Agriculture, like any other industry, utilizes a variety of "inputs" to obtain its production. Naturally it uses a large amount of land. It also uses other sorts of "fixed capital" — buildings, fences, access roads, machinery and equipment of other sorts.[1] It uses "current purchases" of goods from outside the national agricultural sector — fuels, electricity, maintenance and repair of equipment, chemicals, imported feeds, etc. Agriculture uses hired labor, unpaid family labor and the inextricably combined labor and managerial efforts of the farmer himself.

There are two ways to look at the accounts of agriculture. They are equally important, but they originate with different objects in mind. One is based on "profitability" — the return to the farm owner on his inputs of management, labor and capital, operating and fixed. The second is based on a "national farm" concept as it is sometimes called — the value of the output of agriculture in relation to the resources used by agriculture. Ideally the value of these

1. Farm accounting methods naturally differ from farm to farm and from country to country. Individual farmers' accounting methods are heavily influenced by taxation systems. To the extent possible the concept followed here excludes livestock from capital. Moreover, the analysis in general does not include rent and interest, actual or imputed, on farm property, though for most countries it is possible to obtain a figure for "depreciation."

resources used by agriculture should be measured against what their value would be if used in an alternative way, but as will be seen presently, this is difficult to calculate.

For the moment this study is concerned with the "national farm" concept of accounting — the contribution agriculture makes to the gross national product and the relation of total costs to production and output of farms.[2] The object of the inquiry is to establish, to the extent the statistics available will permit, the relative efficiency of agriculture in the various countries of the North Atlantic region.

LAND UTILIZATION

North America has one of the highest ratios of agricultural land per capita in the world and Western Europe one of the lowest. In Canada in the mid–1950s there were 2.21 hectares of arable land and an additional 1.64 hectares of permanent pasture available for each member of the population. In the United States the comparable figures were 0.97 hectares and 1.27 hectares. Both countries had vast areas of rough grazing land in addition.

By contrast there was only about 0.2 hectare of agricultural land per person in the United Kingdom, Switzerland, the Netherlands and Belgium-Luxembourg. Only in Denmark and France was there more than two thirds of a hectare of agricultural land per person (Table 3–1).

In every country of the region more than half of the land in crops other than grasses was used for growing cereals. In the United

2. Agricultural "production" is the duplicated total of everything produced by farming regardless of its utilization; agricultural "output" is production less that part of production which is used up in the process of production by the agricultural industry itself — mainly seed and feedstuffs for livestock. In this discussion a series of further reductions is made: "output" is reduced by the value of "current purchases" of nonlabor inputs used to further agricultural efforts; the resulting value is called "gross agricultural product" or "gross national product originating in agriculture." This figure can then be reduced by the value of depreciation of fixed capital to arrive at a "net agricultural product." A further reduction by the value of wages paid for labor, whether in cash or in kind, results in a value called "operator's income from farming before rent, interest and taxes." Special aspects of these concepts are explained in the course of the discussion.

Table 3–1. Total and Per Capita Agricultural, Arable and Cropped Land, by Country, Mid–1950s   (*Hectares*)

COUNTRY	TOTAL, THOUSANDS			PER CAPITA		
	AGRI-CUL-TURAL[a]	ARA-BLE[a]	CROPPED[a]	AGRI-CUL-TURAL[a]	ARA-BLE[a]	CROPPED[a]
Canada	61,216	35,146	...	3.85	2.21	...
U. S.	374,320	161,460	134,700[b]	2.24	0.97	(0.78)
EEC	69,618	47,930	39,128	0.43	0.30	0.24
BLEU	1,876	1,089	986	0.20	0.12	0.11
France	34,069	21,296	15,881	0.78	0.49	0.37
Germany[c]	14,384	8,744	8,430	0.28	0.17	0.17
Italy	16,979	15,749	12,818	0.35	0.33	0.27
Netherlands	2,310	1,052	1,013	0.21	0.10	0.09
EFTA	29,502	20,786	(14,860)	0.34	0.24	(0.17)
Austria	2,858	1,767	1,307	0.41	0.25	0.19
Denmark	3,047	2,743	2,053	0.68	0.62	0.46
Norway	1,013	828	310	0.29	0.24	0.09
Portugal	4,940[d]	4,130	...	0.56[d]	0.47	...
Sweden	3,884	3,697	2,206	0.53	0.51	0.30
Switzerland	1,191	447	283	0.24	0.09	0.06
U. K.	12,569	7,174	4,701	0.24	0.14	0.09

Sources: OEEC, *Agricultural and Food Statistics,* Paris, 1959; and Appendix I. See also Appendix II, Table A.

a. Agricultural land excludes rough grazing areas; arable land excludes permanent pasture; cropped land excludes temporary grassland.

b. Cropland harvested, of which about 8 million hectares are in nonfood crops.

c. Includes estimate for Saar of 134,000 hectares of agricultural and arable land and 90,000 hectares cropped.

d. Includes rough grazing areas.

States, the United Kingdom and the Scandinavian countries the emphasis was largely on the production of coarse grains, particularly barley, for feed. In Austria, Italy and Switzerland much more land was used for bread grains than for feed grains. Elsewhere the land in cereals was roughly equally divided between wheat and rye on the one hand and barley and oats (and a little corn) on the other.

Large amounts of land were devoted to various sorts of hay and forage crops in the northern countries and Britain, as well as in the Alpine area. Sugar beets and potatoes, alternatively, were very im-

Table 3–2. Land Area Used for Selected Crops Related to Population, by Country, Mid–1950s   (*Hectares per 1,000 Persons*)

COUNTRY	BREAD GRAINS	COARSE GRAINS	POTATOES AND SUGAR BEETS	TEMPO- RARY GRASSES
Canada	607	555	10	...
U. S.	132	339	5	160
BLEU	32	29	17	11
France	105	99	33	125
Germany	54	42	28	5
Italy	102	40	13	61
Netherlands	23	25	20	4
Austria	66	38	32	66
Denmark	40	264	36	155
Norway	6	50	16	150
Portugal	118	106	10	...
Sweden	69	139	24	204
Switzerland	24	11	13	33
U. K.	18	62	11	48

Sources: OEEC, *Agricultural and Food Statistics,* Paris, 1959; and Appendix I.

portant in the Netherlands and Germany, and only somewhat less so in Austria, Belgium-Luxembourg, France and Switzerland (Table 3–2).

Land-use patterns reflect not only topography, climate and the state of technology in agriculture, but agricultural policies as well. In several countries the chief considerations with respect to production policy are protectionist and "balanced output" objectives; in several others these objectives are subordinated to those of supplying at a profit the British and, to less extent, the German markets. Thus Denmark has been content to utilize most of its land for the production of coarse grains and hay crops and to import (in recent years) more than a million tons of feedstuffs in order to produce an exportable surplus of 460,000 tons of meat, 190,000 tons of butter and cheese and more than 100,000 tons of eggs. At the same time the Danes until recently left themselves dependent on imports for about a third of their bread grain requirements. By contrast Sweden is content to attempt to balance its output and consumption of bread grains and to expand its coarse grain output enough to offset the need for feed imports to produce its own livestock product requirements, paying little attention to external demand for meat and dairy products. As a result of these opposite policies, Sweden used in the mid–1950s nearly twice as much land per person for the growing of bread grains and little more than one half as much for coarse grains as did Denmark.

The land-use pattern in Europe is also determined to some extent by the volume of employment in agriculture. As discussed later in this section, one of the major problems of European farming is the smallness of the average farm in many countries. The high density of population on the land means that there is labor available for intensive cultivation. As a result, substantial amounts of land are used for the production of vegetables, potatoes and sugar beets. Even on land in cereals, farmed by modern methods, much more labor is employed in Europe than in North America — a partial explanation of the much higher yields obtained by European farmers.

In some parts of Western Europe there is opportunity for considerable flexibility in land use, should the market — or national policies — demand a shift. The area around the North Sea could be farmed much less intensively, but still very profitably, should the situation warrant this change. It is highly productive in grasses and could easily be adapted to a kind of livestock farming which would employ much less labor per hectare than at present.

Even without much impetus for change from market forces in recent years in Western Europe, some important shifts in land use have been taking place as a result of changing technology. The development of improved strains of wheat and barley and more mechanical land preparation have permitted the sowing of these crops to land formerly limited to rye and oats. Vastly improved yields have resulted from this shift. Similarly, in southern Europe the introduction of hybrid seed has made corn growing much more profitable than formerly as a result of higher yields.

Generally speaking, very little more land could profitably be put under cultivation in Europe in terms of "ploughing up the pastures" without expansion of irrigation in the south. However, consolidation of the very small plots which characterize the farm structure of much of Western Europe would result in a perceptible increase in productive land. It is not uncommon in parts of Europe for access roads and other separation strips to use as much as 10 per cent of the land in richly productive areas where ownership has been subdivided over several generations.

The problem of land fragmentation is very serious in a number of countries on the Continent. The reduction in the nineteenth century in infant and child mortality meant that the average farm owner had more living children at the time of death than owners had had in former times. Thus in those countries where it is customary to divide land equally, fragmentation was accelerated at precisely the time that demand for farm products was rising and — later in the century — that new technology, most effective on larger farm units, was being introduced.

Rising industrialization on the Continent was insufficient to take off the farm the excess population provided by the sharply lowered death rates. Consequently the rural population, most of it unproductively engaged in farming smaller and more widely separated plots of land, increased in most countries until World War I. This development went far to delay technical improvements in agriculture and to waste both land and manpower.[3]

There have been efforts to consolidate fragmented holdings in some countries (and in others, particularly the United Kingdom and the Scandinavian countries, the problem is of minor importance), but success has apparently been limited. Moreover, even if frag-

3. ". . . Medium-sized farms with 100 plots or more are not at all exceptional in badly fragmented districts.

"The inconveniences of fragmentation are — like those of large villages — mainly in the waste of labour and draught power because greater distances have to be travelled to and from work and because work cannot be organized rationally. Moreover, mechanization becomes difficult or, in extreme cases, even impossible. Fragmentation, however, also reduces output because part of the land (up to 10 per cent in some cases) is wasted on the many border lines and because weed control and use of improved seed are hampered. Output per hectare sometimes increases 20 to 30 per cent when land is redistributed and consolidated. Output per man may even increase 50 per cent or more." ECE/FAO, *European Agriculture: A Statement of Problems*, Geneva, 1954, p. 21.

mented holdings were consolidated, most farms in Western Europe would still be extremely small. In fact, in some countries the number of very small holdings is so great as to make their classification as farms dubious (and to make the entire analysis of the input of labor in agriculture very difficult, as subsequent sections of this chapter indicate). In Belgium, for example, 73 per cent of the roughly one million "agricultural holdings" in 1950 were less than one hectare, and only some 60,000 holdings were above ten hectares.[4] This is an extreme case, and a very large number of the "dwarf holdings" of under one hectare in fact do not qualify as farms, as indicated by the fact that the total number of "self-employed" persons in Belgian agriculture, according to the census of 1947, was only 231,000.

However, even in the United Kingdom (in 1958) and Sweden (in 1956), two countries in which fragmentation is of minor importance, about 19 per cent of all farm holdings were less than two hectares. In both countries, though, the number of these small holdings was declining rapidly. In Sweden nearly a third, or about 35,000, of the dwarf holdings disappeared between 1951 and 1956; the number of such holdings decreased in Britain by more than 15,000 between 1952 and 1958, bringing the total to less than 100,000 (Table 3–3).

The very small holdings recorded in these national censuses, less than one or two hectares, should not be considered as real farms, at least for the purposes of establishing farm policies. What might be considered a minimum holding for the full employment of, and a reasonably adequate income for, a farm family naturally will vary widely, depending on many factors.[5] It can almost certainly be as-

4. Statistical data in this section are largely drawn from ECE, *Economic Survey of Europe in 1960,* Geneva, 1961.

5. "It is thought that at least 10–20 ha. of arable land ('basic farms') are required in order to ensure the [Swedish] farm family a reasonable income. . . . [German] labour and entrepreneurship were reasonably remunerated . . . only on sugar beet farms (situated in the most favourable regions and being intensively managed) and on holdings of 50 ha. and over. . . . for the sandy soil regions, 8–9 ha. is generally taken as the minimum size of a farm [in the Netherlands] which is economically and socially justified." OEEC, *Agricultural Policies in Europe and North America,* Second Report, Paris, 1957, pp. 108, 182, 254.

Table 3–3. Number of Holdings by Size, and Changes in Recent Years,[a] Selected Countries, 1950s

COUNTRY	YEAR	THOUSANDS				ANNUAL RATE OF CHANGE (PER CENT)[a]			
		TOTAL	DWARF[b]	SMALL[c]	OTHER	TOTAL	DWARF[b]	SMALL[c]	OTHER
Belgium	1950	991	725	205	61	...	...	...	...
France	1956–57	2,268	385	885	998	(-0.5)	(-0.8)	(-0.6)	(-0.3)
Germany	1959	1,840	625	800	415	-0.9	-0.6	-1.8	+0.7
Italy	1955	4,658		4,330	328	+1.1		+1.1	+1.1
Netherlands	1959	291	60	150	81	-0.5	—	-1.7	—
Austria	1951	433	105	265	63	...	...	...	...
Denmark	1956	199		95	104	-0.5		-1.0	+0.2
Norway	1949	345	200	125	20	...	...	...	...
Sweden	1956	333	65	170	98	-2.5	-7.5	-1.8	—
Switzerland	1955	206	66	97	43	-0.9	-1.0	-1.2	+0.2
U. K.	1958	495	95	100	300	-1.1	-2.8	-1.8	-0.2

Source: ECE, Economic Survey of Europe in 1960, Geneva, 1961, Chap. 3.

a. Change in number of holdings expressed in annual rates from various base years (usually 1949, 1950 or 1951, but 1942 for France and 1939 for Switzerland) to the year shown in Col. 1.

b. Less than 2 hectares; Belgium and the Netherlands, less than 1 hectare.

c. Larger than dwarf holdings but not exceeding 10 hectares; in Austria 20 hectares, in the U. K., 6.1 hectares. Breakdown below 10 hectares is not available for Italy and Denmark. Figures given in table are for all holdings under 10 hectares, but exceeding 0.5 hectares in Italy and 0.55 hectares in Denmark.

sumed, however, that nearly all of those holdings shown in Table 3–3 under the headings of "dwarf" and "small" are not in fact economically viable farm units, if modern production techniques are being employed.[6] Holdings larger than the "dwarf" and "small" categories numbered only 2.5 million in the 1950s (excluding Portugal, for which this information is not available). This represented only a little more than a fifth of all holdings, and probably no more than two fifths of holdings excluding the dwarfs. Only in Denmark, France and the United Kingdom was there a substantial proportion of farm units which appeared to be viable from the standpoint of size.

Moreover, the number of larger farms is increasing very slowly in most countries, despite declines in the numbers of dwarf and small holdings. This indicates that farm consolidation is taking place mainly through acquisition of more land by farmers who already hold more than ten hectares rather than by consolidating small units to form new farms of a viable size.

LABOR

The volume of labor expended in agriculture is a profound mystery in every country. By its nature farming has heavy seasonal fluctuations in the demand for labor. Peak requirements are met by hiring temporary help, by calling on the assistance of members of farm families and by extending the hours of work of everyone called on to help. Periods of low demand are met by reduction in hours worked and by nonagricultural employment of members of farm families, often even of the farm operator himself.

Moreover, part-time farming is very prevalent in industrial countries, regardless of the seasonal factor. In some cases the part-time farm operator works off his farm for other farmers; frequently the part-time farmer works part-time in a nonagricultural occupation; sometimes a full-time nonagricultural worker engages in "farming" as a side line.

6. The exceptions to this generalization would be intensively cultivated vegetable farms close to markets and units concentrating on pigs and poultry fed on purchased feed.

In the United States agricultural census of 1959, after some 232,000 persons who would have been classed as farmers in earlier counts had been screened out, it was found that 36 per cent, or more than a third, of all farm families received more income from work off their farms than from the sale of crops and livestock products. Nearly one half of all farm operators worked off their farms at some time during the year and almost a third worked elsewhere for 100 days or more. Nearly 900,000 of the 1.6 million farm operators who reported sales of less than $2,500 were admittedly part-time farmers depending on outside occupations for most of their income.[7]

In England and Wales about one third of all farm operators in 1959 were said to have produced only some food for their families and small amounts for sale, depending on other occupations for most of their incomes. Only slightly more than half the total of 376,000 separate holdings were of a size sufficient to employ one man fully throughout the year. In France and Italy recent studies indicate that something over half the farms are of insufficient size to employ the farm family and that a quarter to a third of these farm families have outside income. In Germany about half the farms are officially classified as part-time undertakings.[8]

In such circumstances it is easily understood that actual labor devoted to farming is a quantitative unknown. Census questions generally are not very helpful beyond the point of determining the number of people of working age who are available for farm work. Moreover, census questions in the various countries differ so greatly that even comparisons of total "labor force," let alone comparisons of employment by industrial sector are very difficult to make. Sample studies, of course, are used to supplement regular censuses, but

7. Bureau of the Census, *Census of Agriculture, 1959: Preliminary,* Series AC–59–1, Washington, January 1961. The U. S. Department of Agriculture publishes an estimate of man-hours worked on individual crops and livestock products. See *Agricultural Statistics, 1959,* p. 492. It also publishes a figure for "farm employment" (p. 465). If the two figures are related, average labor time per worker is about 1,500 hours per year, or less than 30 hours per week. This is a rough indication of the extent of part-time work in agriculture.

8. ECE/FAO, *European Agriculture in 1965,* Geneva, 1960, mimeo.

in these, too, international comparability is impaired by differences in method.

In many countries in recent years the situation has been complicated, moreover, by rapid changes in farming practices, which undoubtedly have an impact on labor inputs. Thus employment time series are open to doubt even in those cases in which efforts have in fact been made to determine, on the basis of samples, the actual amount of labor which has been going into agriculture.[9]

In view of the statistical uncertainty presented by the available data on labor input in agriculture, it must be recognized that the figures given in Table 3–4 are no more than rough estimates. Column 1 shows the estimated man-years devoted to agriculture by farm operators, unpaid family members and hired labor in 1955. Part-time work has been converted into full-time equivalent by adjusting the total to take account of labor contributed by those only sporadically engaged in agriculture. The author will readily agree with knowledgeable readers that doubt can be cast on every figure in Table 3–4. The margin of error may be considerable in some instances. Seldom, however, would it be wide enough to invalidate the following analysis.

Man-Land Ratios

Based on the estimates of the number of man-years worked in agriculture shown in Table 3–4, it is possible to measure the comparative labor intensity of farming in the various countries. The range is tremendous — from some eighty-two hectares of agricultural land per man-year in Canada to less than three hectares in Italy. In the United States the figure is about sixty-two hectares per man-year. In Europe only the United Kingdom and Sweden show ratios of more than ten hectares to one labor unit. For Western

9. "It can in fact be assumed that the actual volume of employment in agriculture has generally decreased more than available data and estimates would suggest. Not only have people formerly employed in agriculture shifted entirely to other occupations, but others have taken up part-time work where formerly they had none, and those who had a part-time job before have in some cases made the non-farm occupation their main source of income, while farming has become the part-time job." *Ibid.*

Table 3–4. Estimated Number of Man-Years of Labor Input in Agriculture, 1955, and Index, 1950–1959, by Country

COUNTRY	MAN-YEARS, 1955 (THOUSANDS)	INDEX (1955 = 100)									
		1950	1951	1952	1953	1954	1955	1956	1957	1958	1959
Canada	750	121	113	106	104	104	100	96	92	88	(85)
U.S.	6,000	114	110	106	105	104	100	98	93	89	87
EEC	14,060	111	109	107	105	102	100	97	96	93	92
BLEU	300	118	115	109	106	104	100	95	91	89	85
France	(3,800)	109	107	105	104	102	100	99	97	95	94
Germany	3,000	125	120	116	111	105	100	95	91	87	(84)
Italy	6,480	106	105	103	102	101	100	98	97	(95)	(94)
Netherlands	480	109	107	106	104	102	100	98	96	95	93
EFTA[a]	4,170	113	111	108	106	102	100	98	96	94	92
Austria	700	103	102	101	101	100	100	98	97	96	95
Denmark	350	116	113	110	107	105	100	98	94	93	96
Norway	(215)	118	115	109	104	102	100	98	95	92	91
Portugal	(1,300)	..	..	..	..	..	100	..	..	..	..
Sweden	365	133	128	118	113	106	100	97	96	93	87
Switzerland	(280)	109	107	105	104	102	100	98	97	95	94
U.K.	960	112	110	109	107	102	100	99	95	94	93

Sources: Sources shown in Appendix II, text (for Labor, Table B); and ECE, *Economic Survey of Europe in 1960*, Geneva, 1961; USDA, *Agricultural Statistics, 1959* and *1960*, Washington, 1960 and 1961.

a. Portugal is included in estimate of total man-years, excluded from indexes.

Figure 3–1. Estimated Area of Agricultural and Arable Land per Man-Year of Labor, by Country, 1955

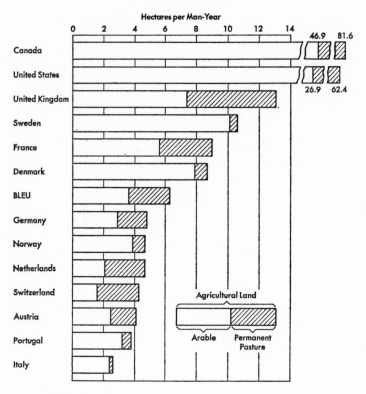

Sources: Tables 3–1 and 3–4.

Europe as a whole the figure is about 5.4 hectares. (See Figure 3–1.)

The range is not narrowed very much if permanent pasture land is deducted from total agricultural land (which, by definition, already excludes rough grazing areas). Canada, with forty-seven hectares of arable land per man-year, contrasts with Switzerland with less than two hectares. The United States figure is about twenty-seven hectares and in Europe only Sweden, Denmark, the United Kingdom and France have more than five hectares of arable land per man-year. For Western Europe the ratio is about 3.7 hectares to one man-year of labor.

It must be kept in mind, however, that many European farmers "use other people's land" in the sense that they import substantial amounts of feedstuffs for animals. Thus the ratios of land to men shown in Figure 3–1 are only very rough gauges of intensiveness, for the manpower figure includes those agricultural workers engaged in producing livestock products from imported feeds. A very rough adjustment for this factor would raise the European ratios to about six hectares of agricultural land and something over four hectares of arable land for each man-year of labor.

What do the European countries get from the much more intensive use of labor in relation to land in agriculture? The answer is complicated, for there are, of course, many factors entering into productivity of land other than the amount of labor expended on it.

Crop production (excluding hay crops) per hectare of land used for crops is higher (except perhaps in Portugal) in every European country than in the United States. (See Appendix II, Table A, and Appendix III, Table E.) In the mid–1950s it ranged from about 60 per cent more in France and 70 per cent more in Italy to well over 200 per cent more in Switzerland and the Netherlands. For Western Europe as a whole crop production per hectare was about 75 per cent greater than in the United States. (This includes an estimate for Portugal, for which precise information is not available.)

Information of a reliable sort as to labor expended on crop production alone is not available. An educated guess, taking into account the greater importance of livestock production in Europe, would place labor input per hectare in crop production in Europe at about four to five times that of the United States, while crop production per hectare is only 75 per cent higher, as noted above.

Table 3–5 compares estimated total agricultural production — livestock and crops (except hay crops) added together in terms of wheat equivalent — in relation to agricultural land and labor input.[10] The first column indicates that production per hectare of agricultural land in Europe is about three times that of the United States

10. The comparisons are not entirely fair because they include in Europe livestock products produced from imported feeds, a matter of considerable importance in Belgium-Luxembourg, Germany, the Netherlands, Switzerland and the United Kingdom. However, an attempt to exclude these products would probably introduce a more serious distortion into the comparisons.

Table 3–5.   Crude Productivity of Land and Labor and Comparative Use of Land and Livestock by Country, Mid–1950s

| COUNTRY | PRODUCTION (WHEAT EQUIVALENT)[a] | | LAND-LIVESTOCK UNITS[b] PER MAN-YEAR |
	KG. PER HA. OF AGRICULTURAL LAND	TONS PER MAN-YEAR OF LABOR INPUT	
Canada	750	61	61
U. S.	1,075[c]	67[c]	44
EEC	3,040	15	7
BLEU	6,130	38	13
France	2,280	20	11
Germany	4,200	19	8
Italy	2,730	7	4
Netherlands	6,800	33	10
EFTA	3,170	22	12
Austria	3,110	13	7
Denmark	5,450	47	20
Norway	3,460	16	11
Portugal	1,170	4	5
Sweden	2,830	30	18
Switzerland	4,870	21	8
U. K.	3,330	43	21

Sources: Tables 3–1, 3–4, Appendix III, Table D; and OEEC, *Agricultural and Food Statistics,* Paris, 1959.

a. Gross production, i.e., simple sum of crop and livestock products according to index described in Appendix III.

b. Sum of hectares of arable land and number of livestock units (calculated as follows: milk cows, 1.00; other cattle, 0.75; horses, 0.80; hogs, 0.30; sheep and goats, 0.10).

c. Includes production of tobacco and fibers (about 8 per cent). Similar adjustment for other countries would be 2.5 per cent or less, with average for Europe and Canada about 1 per cent.

and four times that of Canada. Nowhere in Europe except in Portugal is the ratio less than two to one in comparison to production per hectare in North America.

The second column reveals, however, an even greater disparity in the opposite direction with respect to production per man-year of labor utilized. In this comparison the ratio is about four to one in favor of the North American countries. The European average is pulled down greatly by the low production per man-year in Italy and Portugal. However, the record is also poor in France and Germany as well as in a number of the smaller countries. Though other factors contribute to the disparity, in general, low production per man-year in Europe in comparison to North America reflects the much smaller average size of farms, which cannot be entirely offset by the higher production per hectare of land.

The third column in Table 3–5 provides a partial explanation of the wide disparities shown in the second column. "Land-livestock units" are simply the sum of the number of hectares of arable land and the number of livestock units — a very crude measure of what men had to work with in getting their agricultural production. In Canada the relation between tons of production and land-livestock units per man-year worked was one of parity; in the United States it was about 1.5 to 1; and in Europe about 2 to 1. The higher ratio in Europe is to a large extent explained by the inclusion of livestock products produced from imported feedstuffs.

These measures of comparative productivity and agricultural resources utilized are, of course, very rough. Yet they are probably a reasonable indication of differences in available resources and the methods used in employing them.

What do the Europeans actually get for their concentrated employment of labor on small landholdings (as well as use of feedstuffs from abroad) in comparison to the extensive type of farming which is more typical of North America? Figure 3–2 relates two indexes. The first is an index of "labor intensity" (see source note to the figure). The second is an index of output per land-livestock unit employed. The United States equals 100 in both indexes.

The United Kingdom and Denmark use a little more than double the U. S. manpower per land-livestock unit (as well as important

Figure 3–2.   Index of Labor Intensity and Output per Land-Livestock Unit,[a] by Country, Mid–1950s   (*U. S. = 100*)

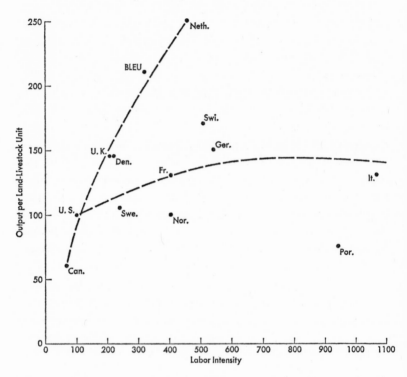

Sources: Labor intensity (man-years worked divided by sum of hectares of arable
land and livestock units) — Appendix II, Tables A and B; and OEEC, *Agricultural
and Food Statistics,* Paris, 1959. Output per land-livestock unit (total output in
wheat equivalent divided by land-livestock units) — Appendix III, Table F; and
OEEC, *op. cit.*
    a. For definition of livestock unit, see Table 3–5, footnote b.

amounts of imported feedstuffs) and obtain about 45 per cent more
final output per land-livestock unit than the United States. Belgium-
Luxembourg employs three times the amount of labor per unit and
obtains twice as much output. These are the best records in Europe.
France uses four times the amount of labor used in the United
States per land-livestock unit and Italy nearly eleven times as much,
but these countries obtain only 30 per cent more output (both
furnish nearly all their own feedstuffs, as does the United States).

Germany, using more than five times the amount of labor, produces only 50 per cent more per land-livestock unit.

To the extent that agriculture in North America and Western Europe can be compared in terms of the measures used here — land, livestock and manpower — it must be concluded that labor in Europe is being employed considerably less efficiently than in the United States.

However, output per man in relation to agricultural resources used is not the whole story. The revolution in agriculture is very much made up of the increasing use of goods and services produced outside the agricultural sector of the economy. These goods and services have great impact on farm production and output. Extension of their use provides the basis for a changing optimum relation between land, livestock, purchased supplies, capital and manpower on the farm. It is to the growing costs of these nonagricultural production aids and their effects on output and profitability of farming that this analysis must now turn.

4

Farm Output and Expenses

Political care and concern for the well-being of farmers have taken many forms, as noted in Chapter 2. In combination these various types of assistance have contributed to a prodigious increase in farm output — generally welcome in most countries, but increasingly embarrassing in a few in recent years.

Apart from balance-of-payments objectives (now much reduced in importance) and the somewhat dubious idea that a considerable degree of self-sufficiency in food production is an important aspect of national defense, agricultural policies have generally been directed toward improving farm incomes. In those countries in which farm output has reached or approached the surplus situation, for one or several commodities, policies for improving farm income give an impression not unlike that of a dog chasing his tail. In assuming that high market prices are a necessary part of income support, governments appear to be on the right path. However, high prices provide a wide spread between costs and revenues for many individual growers. These growers see an advantage in using production techniques which result in more output, putting a downward pressure on prices. This evokes new pressures for price-supporting operations and the sequence is repeated. In desperation acreage control policies are adopted for the surplus products. But due weight is not given to the impact of technology nor to the alternative uses of land taken out of production of particular crops. The result is higher yields of the surplus crop to offset smaller areas under cultivation, while the freed land produces something else which is at least to some extent competitive with the surplus crop. Pressure on prices reappears. Finally, policy calls for taking land out of production entirely — "soil banks" or "approved conservation practices" or other semantically inoffensive names appear in legislation. Payments are made for not producing. But the farmer uses his payment for not farming his poorest land to buy more materials to increase output on his better land. Then the palpable absurdity of the whole system begins to generate resistance in the nonagricultural sectors of society. The most obviously annoying parts of the system must be abandoned — and a retreat begins toward the original dilemma.

Only the United States has run this full cycle in recent years, but other countries in the North Atlantic region have had partial experience with it. If present output and demand trends continue, the problem will become important for an increasing number of European countries.

One result of this pattern of responses to national agricultural policies and their less-than-perfect application has been to hasten a great "industrialization" of agriculture. No matter how much farming is admired as a "way of life" or the yeoman lauded as a bulwark of society,[1] agricultural policies designed to maintain farm incomes have sped the widespread acceptance of agricultural tech-

---

1. "The House Agriculture Committee yesterday reversed itself and put back into the preamble of the general farm bill language praising the family farm type of operation.

"The Committee had received some criticism for its recent action in voting to delete the words 'family farm' from the new farm legislation under consideration by it.

". . . the members, sensitive to the politically potent words 'family farm,' decided today to add to the preamble or declaration of intent in the bill these words:

" 'To recognize the importance of the family farm as an efficient unit of production and as an economic base for towns and cities in rural areas and encourage, promote and strengthen this form of farm enterprise.' " *Washington Post,* July 18, 1961.

niques which depend increasingly on a large volume of purchased supplies and machinery of nonagricultural origin and a large, well-organized and often distant commercial market for all or a large part of farm output.

This process, of course, has been going on for a long time. Farming has moved in the direction of industrialization in North America and parts of Europe for a century. The steam locomotive made possible more regional specialization, the internal combustion engine brought mechanical power to the farm, chemistry supplied artificial fertilizers, improved preservation techniques widened the market for perishable products, rural electrification made possible the mechanization of some farming operations.

In recent years, however, the change has been very rapid. And, because of the policies adopted and the particular circumstances in which they have been applied, these "high-cost–high-output techniques" have been applied by too many farmers having too little land. As a result, despite the income objectives of government policies, farm incomes generally remain unsatisfactory in most countries.

In 1955 farmers in the North Atlantic region purchased nearly $21 billion of operating supplies and services, excluding hired farm labor. Over $12 billion of the total was spent for items originating outside agriculture. This compares to output valued at slightly less than $60 billion.[2] Thus "working capital" needs of farmers amounted to about a third of the value of output (in addition, of course, to the cost of holding feed and seed grown and retained by the farmer).

British farmers, with their heavy dependence on imported feedstuffs, spent nearly half of what they took in for current supplies. About half their expenditure was for seed and feedstuffs. Elsewhere in Europe current purchases amounted to considerably less in rela-

2. Output is the value of sales of farm products plus the value of food consumed by humans on the farms. For the United States, Canada and the United Kingdom the figure includes sales of feed, seed and livestock used by other farmers in the same country. Elsewhere these sales have been deducted from the total output figure. Except in France the amount is probably negligible. Luxembourg, Portugal and Switzerland are excluded from consideration in this chapter. See Appendix II for sources.

tion to the value of output — about a third in most countries, but about a fifth in France and a seventh in Italy. In the United States the figure was about 40 per cent.[3]

The value of farm output less the value of current purchases of production requisites, after adjustment for indirect taxes paid by farm producers and subsidies received by them, is called "gross product at factor cost originating in agriculture" in national accounting terminology. In less fancy language, this is the "value added" by the work and capital of those people engaged in farming before account has been taken of the depreciation of fixed capital employed in agriculture.[4] (See Table 4–1.)

In 1955 gross product originating in agriculture in the North Atlantic region amounted to about $39 billion. Just over half the total was accounted for by the United States and Canada. France, Germany and Italy combined were responsible for 30 per cent. No other country except the United Kingdom accounted for as much as 3 per cent of the total.

This $39 billion of gross product from agriculture represented only 7 per cent of the total gross domestic product of the region in 1955. In no country did agriculture supply as much as a quarter of total product. In the United Kingdom it accounted for less than 5 per cent, in the United States for a little more than that percentage.

Moreover, with the rapid expansion of industrial production in the region, gross agricultural product constituted a steadily declining part of total product during the past decade. Measured in current prices, gross agricultural product as a percentage of total gross

3. However, if the value of "interfarm transactions" is eliminated from both output and purchases, the American figure drops to about a quarter of total output.

4. "Net product at factor cost" is a more desirable measure of the economic value of farming, or any other occupation. This is gross product less depreciation. Estimates of depreciation, however, are peculiarly susceptible to noneconomic or quasi-economic influences. In the main they originate in calculations connected with taxation. Hence they reflect, in agriculture in particular, accounting practices which may well have a political element at least as important as economic considerations. International comparisons of depreciation, and hence of net product, thus have less reliability than international comparisons of gross product, which are themselves subject to very considerable shortcomings.

Table 4–1. Agricultural Output, Current Purchases and Gross Agricultural Product, by Country, 1955   (*Millions*)

COUNTRY	OUTPUT	PURCHASES	GROSS PRODUCT[a]
Canada	$ 2,925[b]	$ (950)[b]	$(1,975)
U. S.	31,660[b]	12,795[b]	19,095
EEC[c]	17,360	3,950	13,355
Belgium	945	310	630
France	5,785	1,200	4,590
Germany	4,385	1,280	3,050
Italy	5,015	710	4,310
Netherlands	1,230	450	775
EFTA[d]	6,645	2,715	4,125
Austria	725	195	525
Denmark	1,020	280	755
Norway	325	95	240
Sweden	750	260	515
U. K.	3,825[b]	1,885[b]	2,090

Sources: Appendix II, Tables C, D and E.

a. At factor cost, except for France, Italy and Denmark. Includes adjustment for inventory changes where available.

b. Includes sales and purchases of domestically produced supplies of agricultural origin used in production.

c. Excludes Luxembourg.   d. Excludes Portugal and Switzerland.

domestic product fell from about 12 per cent in 1951 to somewhat less than 7 per cent in 1958 for the region as a whole.

This fall in the relative importance of agriculture in the total economy did not, of course, mean that farming was a "declining industry." As shown in Chapter 8, agricultural output in the region rose rapidly during the 1950s. But this expansion of output was accompanied by a rapid rise in current expenditures by farmers to obtain a greater volume of supplies (at modestly higher prices in most countries). Moreover, farm prices did not rise as much as other prices in a number of countries during this period. This experience, contrasted with the rapid expansion of industrial production and many services, resulted in a relatively limited growth of gross agricultural product.

Figure 4–1. Percentage Changes in Value of Gross Agricultural Product, Output and Current Purchases, Selected Countries, Annual Average, 1951–1953 to 1956–1958

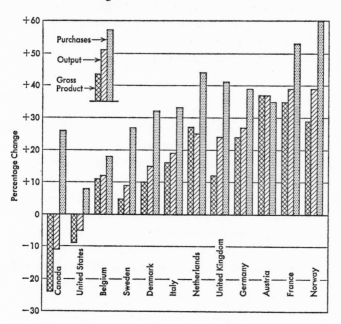

Sources: As shown in Appendix II, text, "Value and Costs."

Only in the United States did the adverse trends in costs and prices completely overcome the effect of higher farm output. The especially favorable year of 1958 stands alone in the latter part of the decade as one in which the value of agricultural product was nearly as great as in the record years of the beginning of the decade. In Canada cost and price problems were combined with lower output to depress agricultural product.

Thus the experience in Europe in the 1950s differed considerably from that in North America. In every country in Europe the value of current purchases rose rapidly and it was accompanied by a rise in the value of output. While the percentage increase in the value of output was not so great as that in current purchases (except in Austria), it was sufficient in absolute money values to provide for an increase in gross agricultural product ranging from about 1 per cent to 6 per cent annually. In North America, on the other hand, expenditures for current purchases rose (though not so rapidly as in Europe) but the value of output fell, and with it — and at a more rapid pace — the gross agricultural product. American and Canadian farmers were running faster but, unlike the Red Queen, were unable to stay in the same place (Figure 4–1).

PRICES

To some extent the differences in developments in North America and in Europe over the 1950s resulted from price factors. Among the countries for which reasonably reliable data are available,[5] only Canada, the United States and Belgium showed declines in prices received by farmers, and in Belgium the rise in the volume of output was sufficient to offset the price decline and provide for a rise of 12 per cent in the value of output between 1951–1953 and 1956–1958. In Sweden the situation was reversed, with production falling somewhat but with higher prices more than offsetting the effect of this. Elsewhere both the volume of output and prices rose. In France, Norway and Austria price increases accounted for more of the rise in value of output than did volume. (See Table 4–2.)

In most countries prices of current operating supplies and services were reasonably steady over the 1950s.[6] Nearly everywhere the volume of purchased supplies rose more rapidly than the volume of

5. The constant price data used here are derived mainly from unpublished data collected by the ECE. The figures for the United Kingdom are estimates based on the physical agricultural output index and constant price index for gross product originating in agriculture, forestry and fishing, together with the ECE data. United States data are from USDA, *Agricultural Statistics 1959*, Washington, 1960. For Canada, index of price paid and received used as deflator. See FAO *Monthly Bulletin*, Rome, November 1961.

6. In the European countries other than the United Kingdom "current purchases" exclude purchases of domestic seed and feedstuffs. In the United Kingdom, Canada and the United States such transactions are included in "current purchases." The decline in prices paid by farmers over this period in the United States is entirely due to lower prices for supplies of agricultural origin. This, of course, is also reflected in lower value of output, as sales of such items are included in that value.

Table 4–2. Estimated Changes in Value, Volume and Prices of Agricultural Output and Current Purchases, Selected Countries, Annual Average, 1951–1953 to 1956–1958

| | INDEX: 1951–1953 = 100 | | | | | |
| | OUTPUT | | | CURRENT PURCHASES | | |
COUNTRY	VALUE	VOL-UME	PRICES	VALUE	VOL-UME	PRICES
Canada	88	94	(94)ᵃ	126	119	106
U. S.	95	110	86	108	112	96
EEC						
Belgium	112	117	96	118	109	108
France	139	113	123	153	148	103
Germany	127	114	111	139	136	102
Italy	119	112	106	133	135	99
Netherlands	125	120	104	144	146	99
EFTA						
Austria	137	114	120	135	114	118
Norway	139	114	122	160	133	120
Sweden	109	97	112	127	111	114
U. K.	124	115	(108)	141	(131)	(108)

Sources: As shown in Appendix II, text ("Value and Costs").

a. Implied price index; official index of prices received by farmers shows decline to 87. FAO, *Monthly Bulletin,* Rome, November 1961.

output. The tendency toward diminishing returns in output in relation to additional purchased supplies was stronger in some countries than in others, however. In the United States a 12 per cent increase in volume of current purchases was related to a 10 per cent rise in volume of output (Table 4–2). This was a period, however, when land in crops in the United States declined by about 7 per cent and animal numbers remained nearly steady. Purchased supplies were thus applied to a somewhat smaller "national farm" in the latter part of the decade.

In France and the Netherlands the volume of purchased supplies rose by nearly half but volume of output increased by only 13 and 20 per cent, respectively. Germany and Italy registered expansions in volume of purchases of more than a third while volume of output increased at less than half that rate. The record in the United Kingdom was a little better, with the volume of purchased supplies rising by about a third while output increased by a sixth. In Belgium the volume of agricultural output rose much more rapidly than the volume of purchased supplies.

MARGINAL RETURNS

While the "real" percentage increments to output were generally well below the percentage increments to purchased supplies, analysis of the money returns and expenditures is more illuminating. Farmers, like other entrepreneurs, spend money to make money.

In the United States an outlay of $1.5 billion more per year in 1956–1958 than in 1951–1953 was accompanied by a decline in value of output of approximately the same amount.[7] As noted above, the decline in value of output was due entirely to a steep fall in farm prices, averaging about 14 per cent over the period in the United States. (See Table 4–3.)

In Europe, however, additional outlays for current operating purposes were generally profitable. In France and Italy, two countries in which prices of production requisites were stable and the volume of purchases rose sharply, each dollar of incremental current outlay was related to about three dollars' worth of incremental output. In Austria, Belgium, Denmark, Germany and Norway incremental returns were worth about twice as much as incremental outlays. In the United Kingdom an additional outlay of $1 was related to added output worth about $1.50. In the Netherlands and Sweden — both making substantial modifications to their agricultural policies during this period — more expenditures brought little or no net increase in money returns.

To a very considerable extent the incremental income — the excess of the additional value of output over the additional current expenditures (including depreciation) — during this period in Eu-

---

7. The figures used here for outlays include both current supplies and depreciation on capital. The latter figure is unquestionably less reliable than others used in this chapter.

Table 4–3. Increments to Value of Output and to Value of Current Purchases and Depreciation, and Influence of Price Changes, Selected Countries, Annual Average, 1951–1953 to 1956–1958

| COUNTRY | INCREMENTAL VALUE (MILLIONS) | | INCREMENTAL OUTPUT AS PER CENT OF INCREMENTAL COSTS | |
	OUT-PUT	PURCHASES AND DE-PRECIATION	AT ACTUAL PRICES	AT "PARITY" PRICES[a]
Canada	$ –385	$ 288	–134	–73
U. S.	–1,551	1,522	–102	129
EEC				
Belgium	111	60	185	393
France	1,944	(687)	(283)	(121)
Germany	1,052	522	202	122
Italy	816	274	298	135
Netherlands	273	257	106	78
EFTA				
Austria	206	93	222	206
Denmark	141	82	172	...
Norway	103	53	194	179
Sweden	70	76	92	236
U. K.	816	551	148	125

Sources: As shown in Appendix II, text ("Value and Costs").
a. Based on assumption that prices of agricultural products changed at same rate as those for current purchases.

rope was attributable to the fact that prices received by farmers rose more rapidly than those paid by farmers.[8] No better tribute could be paid to the political persuasiveness of European farmers than this record of rising prices in a period of growing surpluses of the basic commodities on the world market.

8. The price data used here are based on unpublished data provided by governments in Europe to the ECE. It should be noted that they differ, in some cases radically, from price indexes published elsewhere, e.g., in FAO, *Monthly Bulletin,* Rome, May 1960.

The final column in Table 4–3 indicates what the relationship of incremental purchases and depreciation to incremental output between 1951–1953 and 1956–1958 would have been if prices paid to farmers had moved at the same rate as the prices of their purchased supplies. In all of the Common Market countries except Belgium the incremental income would have been cut substantially, and in the Netherlands it would have been less than incremental costs (because of a decline in prices of imported feedstuffs). The relationship between incremental output and costs in Austria, Norway and the United Kingdom would have remained substantially unchanged, but that in Sweden and the United States would have been vastly improved.

While much of the incremental margin between value of output and costs of purchases and depreciation depended on price increases for farm products in Europe, it would still have been profitable for farmers in most countries to have made the additional expenditures, even if considerably lower price levels had been maintained, assuming that the prices early in the decade were "reasonable."

CAPITAL EXPENDITURES

At the same time that farmers were spending more for current supplies, they were also rapidly accumulating more fixed capital. In every country for which data are available capital outlays during the 1950s regularly exceeded the depreciation allowances. (See Appendix II, Table F.)

Not too much reliance should be placed on the figures shown in Table 4–4. What constitutes investment varies in definition from country to country and, as indicated earlier, depreciation estimates are highly suspect, viewed from a purely economic standpoint. Moreover, there were price increases for capital items over the 1950s. Nevertheless, it is significant that farmers in the European countries spent about $1 billion more for gross capital investment in 1958 than they did in 1951, while there was little change in the United States. Perhaps more important (to the extent the depreciation figures can be trusted) is the fact that net investment in agri-

Table 4–4. Gross and Net Fixed Capital Formation in Agriculture, Selected Areas, 1951, 1955 and 1958   (*Millions*)

YEAR	U. S.	EEC[a]	EFTA[b]
	GROSS		
1951	$4,825	$1,170[c]	$510[d]
1955	4,230	1,680	600
1958	4,525	2,080	725
	NET		
1951	1,600	405[c]	200[d]
1955	510	670	175
1958	565	740	210

Source: Appendix II, Table F.
a. Excludes Luxembourg and the Saar.   b. Excludes Portugal and Switzerland.
c. Includes 1953 figure for Belgium instead of 1951.
d. Includes 1953 figure for Denmark instead of 1951.

cultural fixed capital in Europe went up steadily over the 1950s and by 1958 was substantially higher than in the United States.[9]

If the investment figures shown in Table 4–4 are related to the estimated data for labor input in agriculture (Table 3–4), it is apparent that European agriculture is now adding to its fixed capital per man-year at a rate not much lower than that in the United States. (In a number of countries it is higher, particularly if deductions for farm housing are made from the American figure.) However, the gross investment per man-year worked in agriculture in the United States remains substantially above that in Europe — about $850 per man-year in 1958 against something like $175 in Europe.

In terms of investment per hectare of land, however, the European figure is far above that in the United States. The American figure for net investment in the mid–1950s was below $4 per hectare

9. To the extent they can be compared, farm equipment prices in Europe and the United States are not much different. However, construction costs are considerably lower in Europe. Further, figures for the United States include investment in residential construction and depreciation of residential buildings. The estimates for most of the European countries appear to exclude these items. A large part of the total net farm investment in the United States in 1958 was for residential construction.

of arable land. In the EEC countries net investment per hectare was about four times that amount and in Austria, Denmark, Norway, Sweden and the United Kingdom (taken together) almost as much. Even gross capital formation in Europe, much more modest in total than in the United States, exceeded that of the United States per unit of land. Thus European agriculture is becoming increasingly capital-intensive as well as remaining much more labor-intensive than farming in the United States.

INCOME PATTERNS

The decline in labor input in agriculture described in the preceding chapter thus has been combined with a rise in expenditures for current operating supplies and (in Europe) a rapid advance in capital expenditures. Combined with the rise in volume of output (except in Sweden) and prices (except in the United States, Canada and Belgium), these factors have resulted in a considerable increment to the value of output and net product per full-time worker in agriculture in recent years (Table 4–5).

In current prices the value of output per man-year rose between 1951 and 1958 by $1,000 or more in the United States, Denmark, the Netherlands, Sweden and the United Kingdom (where the increase was nearly $1,600). Increases of nearly $1,000 were also recorded in France, Germany and Norway. In these three countries the percentage increase in the value of output per man-year over this period was 80 per cent or more. In most other European countries (Belgium excepted) the rise in output per man-year was roughly 50 per cent, in the United States something over 20 per cent (despite falling prices) and in Canada 10 per cent.

With the rise in expenditure for current operating supplies and depreciation, however, net product per man-year showed a less dramatic increase in most countries, and in Canada net product actually declined. In the United States net product per full-time person in agriculture increased by about $350, or 11 per cent, between 1951 and 1958 but about half this increase was accounted for by additional subsidies. In France, Germany, Norway and the Netherlands net product rose by some 60 to 75 per cent (though in

Table 4–5. Value per Man-Year of Labor of Output, Current Purchases and Depreciation and Net Product, 1955, and of Increments, 1951–1958, Selected Countries

COUNTRY	VALUE, 1955			INCREMENTS, 1951–1958		
	OUT-PUT	CURRENT PURCHASES AND DEPRECIATION	NET PROD-UCT[a]	OUT-PUT	CURRENT PURCHASES AND DEPRECIATION	NET PROD-UCT[a]
Canada[b]	$3,900	$1,650	$(2,250)	$ 410	$ 900	$(-380)
U.S.[b]	5,280	2,750	2,560	1,300	1,120	350
EEC						
Belgium	2,820	1,070	1,740	520	270	280
France[c]	1,520	(400)	(1,120)	900	(300)	(600)
Germany	1,460	510	940	960	420	550
Italy[c]	720	150	570	260	70	190
Netherlands	2,510	1,030	1,470	1,000	550	690
EFTA						
Austria	1,030	380	650	430	210	210
Denmark[c]	2,920	930	2,030	(1,070)	(430)	(650)
Norway	1,510	670	880	810	420	380
Sweden	2,340	1,010	1,410	1,050	590	470
U.K.[b]	3,990	2,160	1,980	1,580	1,220	450

Sources: Appendix II, Tables C, D, E and F; and Table 3–4.
a. At factor cost. Where Cols. 3 and 6 do not equal difference between preceding columns, adjustment has been made for inventory changes.
b. Includes sales and purchases of domestically produced agricultural commodities used for production.
c. At market prices.

Table 4-6. Comparison of Gross Product per Man-Year in Agriculture and in Other Industries, Selected Countries and Years, 1951–1958

| COUNTRY | INDEX OF VALUE OF GROSS PRODUCT IN AGRICULTURE AND IN OTHER INDUSTRIES (1951 = 100) | | | | | | VALUE OF GROSS PRODUCT, 1958 | |
| | AGRICULTURE | | | OTHER INDUSTRIES | | | AGRICULTURE | OTHER INDUSTRIES |
	1951	1955	1958	1951	1955	1958		
Canada	100	80	95	100	126	147	$3,115	$5,690
U.S.	100	90	117	100	117	131	4,145	6,770
EEC								
Belgium	100	122	148	100	112	127	(2,830)	3,170
France	100	129	176	100	140	189	1,645a	2,495a
Germany	100	130	174	100	142	170	1,370	2,090
Italy	100	127	143	100	141	159	750	1,655
Netherlands	100	126	158	100	137	165	2,020	2,235
EFTA								
Austria	100	139	158	100	138	166	850	1,475
Denmarkb	100	127	145	100	110	131	2,460	2,260
Norway	100	148	172	100	119	139	1,300	2,850
Sweden	100	119	142	100	121	144	1,690	3,375
U.K.	100	123	138	100	120	140	2,450	2,375

Sources: Appendix II, Tables B and E; and OEEC, *General Statistics,* Paris, January 1961.

a. At exchange rate of 4.90 (new francs) per dollar.

b. Figures for gross product in agriculture include gross product originating from dairy and slaughterhouse operations; labor input estimates used in the calculations exclude employment in these operations.

the Netherlands about a third of the rise was due to increased subsidies paid to farmers). Elsewhere in Europe the gains were somewhat more modest, but still substantial.

Despite these sharp gains in product per man-year in agriculture, farmers in most countries did not improve their lot in comparison to urban workers. Table 4–6 compares gross agricultural product (before allowance for depreciation of capital but including subsidies) per man-year in agriculture with gross product per employed person outside agriculture. While these figures are not quite comparable to personal income data, which would be more desirable if available for all countries, they are probably indicative of the relative sizes of personal incomes (which are considerably lower than the amounts shown in the final two columns).

Only in Belgium, Germany, Denmark and Norway did average gross product improve more rapidly in agriculture than in other occupations from 1951 to 1958. In most other European countries farmers failed, on the average, to hold their own in comparison to their urban counterparts. In Canada and the United States this failure was of considerable magnitude.

Gross product per man-year in agriculture was approximately equal to that in industry only in Denmark,[10] the Netherlands and the United Kingdom in 1958. It is interesting to note that of these countries the United Kingdom and Denmark ranked high among the European countries in terms of land per man-year worked. All three ranked high in terms of expenditures for production requisites per man and per hectare. Farm prices in Denmark and the Netherlands were the lowest in Europe. The United Kingdom and the Netherlands made the most extensive use of the deficiency-payment system of price support.

The problem of inadequate size of farms in most countries in Europe is demonstrated sharply in the context of value of output and gross agricultural product. The value of output and gross prod-

10. The Danish figure for agricultural gross product is somewhat overstated, as it includes value added by dairy and slaughterhouse operations, while the labor input estimate does not include employment in these operations. In both the Netherlands and the United Kingdom the amount is raised by direct payments by governments to farmers.

Figure 4–2.   Value of Output and Gross Agricultural Product per Hectare of Agricultural Land and Average Number of Hectares per Man-Year Worked, Selected Countries, 1955

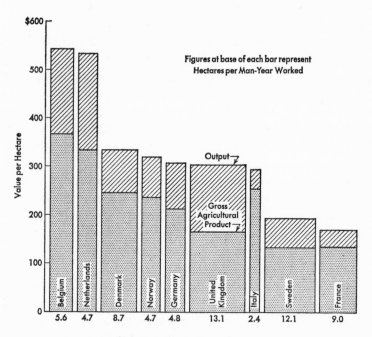

Sources: Appendix II, Tables A, B, C and E.

uct per hectare of agricultural land in several countries is shown vertically in the bars in Figure 4–2. The width of each bar indicates the average number of hectares per man-year worked. The area of each rectangle thus formed, therefore, indicates the value of output and gross product per man-year in agriculture in 1955.

The low level of output and gross product per man-year in Germany, for example, is clearly due to inadequate land. In Denmark and the United Kingdom the value of output per hectare is roughly equal to that in Germany, but larger average landholdings raise gross returns to the farmer far above the German level. The same point is even more applicable to Italy, where value of output and of gross product per hectare is in the same general range as in Denmark and the United Kingdom but value per man-year is very low due to the tiny average landholding per full-time worker of only 2.4 hectares.

France and Sweden appear to present a slightly different problem in that neither output nor gross product per hectare is very high, although the average size of holding per full-time worker is relatively large. Agriculture in both countries tends to be more or less self-contained and balanced with respect to production and consumption patterns. Neither country uses large amounts of purchased materials in relation to land area. Yet, on closer analysis the problem in these countries is not in fact so different. Both countries have considerable areas of relatively poor agricultural land, by European standards. Very intensive farming of the sort practiced in much of Europe is not profitable in large parts of Sweden and France. The average size of farm required to employ fully a farm family would tend to be considerably larger in these countries than in, say, Denmark or the Netherlands.

While the optimum ratio of land to labor in any part of Europe will probably never approach that prevailing in the United States or Canada, it can hardly be doubted that European agriculture in general cannot be both productive and profitable (even at the uncompetitive prices prevailing in most countries) unless fewer people attempt to obtain their living from the land. That some people are leaving the land has been shown in the preceding chapter. Whether they are leaving rapidly enough to assure adequate incomes for those remaining without price increases decreed by governments and more autarkical production policies and even less international specialization is a question which requires further examination, but first we must carry the analysis of income from farming one stage further.

5

Income of Farmers

The preceding chapter has described the extent to which growing expenses of agriculture have eaten away at total revenues from farming and the resultant relatively slow growth of agriculture's contribution to gross and net national product. At the same time, however, the numbers of people engaged in farming have been falling. The upshot has been an improvement in the contribution to national product per man-year of those remaining in agriculture, but the improvement has not been quite at the same rate (in most countries) as the growth in GNP originating with each person outside agriculture.

The part of the value of total farm output (including subsidies) left after making deductions for current purchases of production requisites and depreciation on capital has been called "net national product." It represents what remains to be divided between "labor income" and "profits" (before meeting interest charges and the cost of rents, whether actual or imputed).

A first approximation of the profitability of farming (without discriminating between the farmer as a wage earner and as a capitalist) can be had merely by deducting wages paid to hired workers from the value of net agricultural product. Between 1951 and 1958 total profits (as defined in this way) fell sharply in Canada — by more than a third. In the United States the decline was also great, about 13 per cent. Wage costs in both countries rose only moder-

Table 5–1. Wages Paid to Farm Workers and Net Income (Profits)[a] of Farm Operators, 1958, and Changes, 1951–1958, by Country

	TOTAL, 1958 (MILLIONS)		INDEX (1951 = 100)	
COUNTRY	WAGES	PROFITS	WAGES	PROFITS
Canada	$ 180	$ 1,590	104	65
U. S.	2,880	15,145	103	87
EEC				
Belgium	60	570	125	112
France	785	4,660	147	153
Germany	675	2,570	132	123
Italy	640	3,575	104[b]	114[b]
Netherlands	170	695	135	143
EFTA				
Denmark	170	560	100	123
Norway	25	180	96	144
Sweden	100	395	138	96
U. K.	985	1,100	138	109

Sources: See Appendix II, text (sources for Table B).
a. Before deductions for interest and rent.   b. 1954 = 100.

ately, and the chief cause of the decline was the fall in prices received by farmers.

In the European countries for which this measure is possible all but Sweden registered greater operator profits. Wage payments increased everywhere but in Norway and in Denmark, but a combination of more output and (in most countries) higher prices was more than enough to offset the larger wage bill and other additional operating costs (Table 5–1).

AVERAGE INCOME FROM FARMING

How many farmers are there? An "economic answer" to this question is as difficult as to that concerning the total amount of labor expended in agriculture, which is discussed in Chapter 3. Part-time farming is so prevalent that employment classification, even where censuses and sample studies make thorough analyses of the sources of income, is extremely difficult.

Yet the number of farm families is a factor crucial to the ultimate amelioration of the farm income problem. No solution of agricultural problems in any of the industrialized countries of the North Atlantic region can be reached without adaptation of the number of farmers to the modern techniques of farming and livestock raising which are now available to people on the land. Governments throughout the region would be well advised to study in great detail the whole question of part-time farming and its economic position, while making increasingly intensive analyses of what constitutes a viable farm for a full-time operator and his family.[1] It might well be discovered that one aspect of the solution of farm income problems is increased efficiency, rather than abolition, of part-time farm operation in certain areas in many countries.

What we must be content with here are some estimates of the number of "full-time farm operator equivalents," i.e., the sum of full-time operators and part-time operators converted to the equivalents of full-time operators. It must be understood that these estimates are very rough.

Table 5–2 shows estimates of the number of full-time family units and the number of man-years of family labor. By dividing these estimates into the estimates of farm income (before deduction of interest and rent) shown in Table 5–1 an estimate is reached of the average income in 1958 of a full-time farm operator and his family. Estimated income per man-year of family labor expended on agriculture is shown in the final column of Table 5–2.

The "profit" (before allowance for interest and rent) of the average full-time farm family, shown in the third column of Table 5–2, varies widely from country to country.[2] This, of course, is to be expected, given the wide differences in resources available to the average farmer in the various countries.

1. See OEEC, *Agricultural Policies,* Second and Fifth Reports, Paris, 1957 and 1961. Also, ILO, *Why Labour Leaves the Land,* Geneva, 1959.

2. The figures for Norway and Sweden are misleadingly low, as they do not reflect incomes of farmers working forest and woodland on their own farms. These are said to amount to as much as 20 per cent of farm income in Sweden. ILO, *Why Labour Leaves the Land,* Geneva, 1960.

Table 5–2. Estimated Man-Years of Farm Family Labor and Average Incomes from Farming, Selected Countries, 1958

| COUNTRY | MAN-YEARS WORKED[a] | | AVERAGE INCOME[b] | |
	BY OPERA-TORS	BY OPERA-TORS AND OTHER FAMILY MEMBERS	PER OPERA-TOR'S FAMILY	PER MAN-YEAR OF FAMILY LABOR
Canada	375	560	$4,240	$2,840
U. S.	3,000	4,200	5,050	3,610
EEC				
Belgium	150	205	3,800	2,780
France	1,800	3,000	2,590	1,550
Germany	1,100	2,100	2,340	1,220
Italy	2,350	4,700	1,520	760
Netherlands	210	350	3,310	2,000
EFTA				
Denmark	170	210	3,290[c]	2,670[c]
Norway	130	180	1,380	1,000
Sweden	210	275	1,880	1,440
U. K.	260	300	4,230	3,670[d]

Sources: Estimates of farm family labor — Appendix II, Table B; income — Table 5–1.

a. Estimated full-time equivalent of both full-time and part-time work of operators and other family members.

b. Before interest and rent.

c. Includes income from dairy and slaughterhouse operations in Denmark.

d. Man-year figure overstated because only wives counted in addition to operator.

In Table 5–3 an attempt is made to measure profit per farm family in relation to the farm resources used (arable land plus livestock units) and the purchase of current operating supplies, wages and depreciation on capital. The second column reflects to a very considerable extent (though not entirely) the high prices prevailing in the EEC countries as compared to other countries in the region. At Danish prices, for example, profit per land-livestock unit would have been below the Danish figure of $76 in most of the EEC countries (as well as in the other countries).

The last column demonstrates the very great extent to which French and Italian farmers depend on their own labor (and that of

Table 5–3. Income of Farm Operators in Relation to Use of Resources, by Country, 1958

COUNTRY	LAND-LIVESTOCK UNITS[a]		INCOME PER $1,000 EXPENDITURE ON WAGES, OPERATING SUPPLIES AND CAPITAL[c]
	NUMBER PER FULL-TIME FARM OPERATOR[b]	INCOME PER UNIT	
Canada	124	$ 34	$1,030[d]
U. S.	83	61	680[d]
EEC			
Belgium	25	150	1,240
France	23	111	1,595
Germany	22	105	975
Italy	11	135	1,945
Netherlands	23	145	915
EFTA			
Denmark	43	76	1,075
Norway	17	79	900
Sweden	32	59	880
U. K.	81	52	330[d]

Sources: Tables 5–1 and 5–2 and Appendix II, Tables D and F; OEEC, *Agriculture,* Paris, 1961.

a. Sum of hectares of arable land and number of livestock units.

b. Man-years worked by operators (Col. 1, Table 5–2) are, for purposes of this calculation, considered the equivalent of full-time farm operators.

c. Capital represented by depreciation. Profit calculated before interest and rent.

d. Operating supplies include interfarm transactions. Exclusion of these purchases would raise profit figures by approximately 15 per cent in Canada, 40 per cent in the United States and possibly 5 per cent in the United Kingdom.

their families) and the natural fertility of their land to make a profit from farming. Their outlays for hired labor and production requisites are only one half to two thirds their profits (before interest and rent). The contrast with the British situation is striking. There an outlay of $1,000 brings a profit of only a third that much. Yet the average full-time British farmer, because he has a larger farm and carries a much larger number of livestock units, makes substantially more profit.[3] His income, computed in this way, compares very favorably with that of the average full-time farmer in Canada and the United States, despite the fact that he makes much larger outlays of money per dollar of income.

CAPITAL COSTS

The analysis above does not take account of the charges against the farmer's income for interest on capital invested and rents (whether actually paid or imputed). The Economic Commission for Europe has calculated an imputed interest cost in seven countries in an effort to arrive at a figure it calls "farm family labor income."[4] A somewhat similar computation has been made here for the United States and Canada.

This deduction for capital charges reduces farm income by 10 to 20 per cent in Canada, the United States, Belgium, France, Germany and the United Kingdom (the Netherlands would probably fall in this group if the ECE data were complete for that country). In Norway and Sweden this deduction lowers farm incomes by about a quarter and in Italy by about 40 per cent.

To the extent this interest cost is in fact paid on farm debts, it represents a real lowering of farm income. However, to the degree the farmer has an unencumbered equity in his farm, it can be allocated to him as an "agricultural capitalist" and added to his income as an "agricultural laborer" and "farm manager."

INCOME PROSPECTS

These incomes of farm operators, not very satisfactory in comparison to those of their urban compatriots in most countries, have been achieved in recent years by a combination of factors outlined

3. The British farmer, of course, receives sizable payments from the government under the deficiency-payment system. However, this probably does not exceed, as a percentage of the total, the extra income received by French and Italian farmers as a result of protection from foreign competition.

4. *Economic Survey of Europe in 1960,* Geneva, 1961, Chap. 3.

earlier in this volume — the continued use of protectionist techniques, in many cases guaranteed prices, improved farming techniques, more capital and operating supplies and a steady reduction in the number of people attempting to gain their living from farming without causing a commensurate reduction in land used for agriculture.

In Europe — but not in the United States and Canada — these income-raising factors have been supported in recent years by another: rather rapid improvement in dietary standards of the general populace. It is to this aspect of the problem that the next two chapters are devoted.

Here it is enough to anticipate the findings given later by pointing out that this expansion of demand will continue at a much more modest rate in the future. European farmers — and governments — will find themselves, like their American counterparts in recent years, bereft of one of the important elements making for comparative ease in obtaining rising farm incomes.

It is in this context that the common agricultural policy of the EEC must be seen and judged. Designed as it is primarily for income support of agricultural populations, it will necessarily be employed strongly against imports of foods, if it is to have as one of its results a continued rise in the demand for European farm products at rates approaching those of the recent past. Because European agriculture in total is highly diversified, the pressure for substituting domestic output for imports will affect nearly every temperate agricultural product. At first most of the pressure will be on dairy products and cereals, but the tendency toward exclusion will continue to grow for other products as well.

As physical surpluses of some commodities in Europe become more usual, the problems of income support for farmers will become much more complex — as the American experience has so vividly demonstrated. And with these complexities will come more of the international frictions which have already marked negotiations on trade in farm products.

6

Levels of
Food Consumption

The peoples of the fifteen countries under consideration here comprise a very large proportion of that part of the world's population which is, on the average, adequately fed. The 460 million people in the region have consumed in recent years an average of slightly more than 3,000 calories per person per day.[1] This is about 50 per cent more than the average person consumes in the Far East, the Middle East and the poorer countries of Africa and perhaps 10 to 20 per cent more than the average in the rest of the world (Table 6–1).

This average of some 3,000 calories is generally deemed adequate by nutritionists and physiologists. Moreover, the quality of the diets in the region, as measured by availability of the important nutrients, is also high in comparison to diets in most of the rest of the world. In North America the average person consumes about 65 grams of animal proteins daily, in Western Europe about two thirds that amount. By contrast, the people of Japan and Egypt consume only about a third as much animal protein as the people of Western Europe and the people of India less than a tenth as much.

1. Sources used in this section are the same as those shown in Appendix III, Tables A–C.

Table 6–1. Estimated Daily Per Capita Consumption of Chief Nutrients, Selected Countries and Regions, Mid–1950s

REGION OR COUNTRY	CALORIES	ANIMAL PROTEIN (GRAMS)	PER CENT OF CALORIES FROM		
			CEREALS AND PO- TATOES	LIVE- STOCK PROD- UCTS[a]	FATS AND OILS[b]
North Atlantic region					
North America	3,150	65	25	35	16
EEC	2,850	41	46	20	17
EFTA	3,120	47	36	26	16
Australia	3,230	59	31	33	12
India	1,890	5	68	5[b]	5[a]
Japan	2,070	14	75	2	3
Egypt	2,580	13	71	8[b]	4[a]
Brazil	2,520	18	50	13	6
Chile	2,550	28	59	14	8

Source: FAO, *Production Yearbook, 1958*, Rome, 1959.
a. Excludes butter.   b. Includes butter.

RECENT CONSUMPTION LEVELS

Measured by the most basic indicator of volume — the number of calories available per person daily — food consumption in most of the countries of the region has been remarkably stable in recent years. (See Figure 6–1.) Since 1950 the number of calories available per person has varied by less than 3 per cent above or below the average for the period 1950–1959, and in many countries the year-to-year variations have been even smaller. Only in Italy, Denmark and the United Kingdom has there been a persistent rise in caloric intake — and in the last two countries that trend has now apparently halted. Moreover, average consumption of calories in nearly every country has been within a few percentage points of the average for all the countries taken together. Only Italy and Portugal,

Figure 6–1.   Average Number of Calories Available per Person
per Day, 1959, and Range of Average Calories Available,
1948–1950 to 1959, by Country

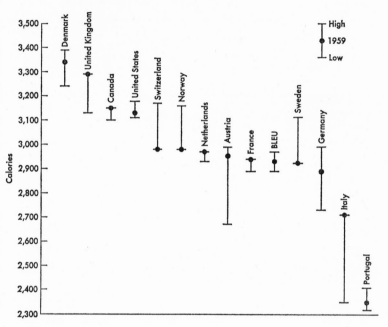

Source: FAO, *Production Yearbook, 1960,* Rome, 1961.

below the average, and Denmark and the United Kingdom, above
the average, are major exceptions to this generalization.

Poverty limits the volume of food intake in individual cases in
all countries. But the volume of food consumption of the general
population, measured solely by the number of calories, is seriously
limited by income only in Italy and Portugal. Consumer surveys
made in a number of countries show that the differences in caloric
intake of persons in different income groups are not marked, except
at the very lowest income levels.

Proteins

These surveys, however, do show great differences by income
group in the structure of diets. It appears that men almost univer-

sally prefer much of their food "converted" into animal products, if they can afford it. It is much more expensive to maintain life by eating meat, milk, poultry and eggs than by eating products directly from the soil. A ton of wheat, milled to produce about three quarters of a ton of flour, has roughly the same caloric value as a ton of meat. The people of the thirteen countries of Western Europe considered here in recent years fed their animals an average of nearly three tons of cereals and other feed concentrates (as well as large amounts of grasses) for each ton of meat (including meat equivalent of eggs and milk). Viewed from a purely economic standpoint, livestock products are a luxury available only to those in a position to "waste" a part of their land resources in order to please their palates.

The nutritionist measures this tendency to favor animal products in terms of consumption of animal proteins. Proteins present in vegetable foodstuffs are equally valuable in the maintenance of health.[2] In most of the countries of the North Atlantic region the average person consumes between 85 and 100 grams of protein — vegetable and animal — per day, and in even the poorest countries — Italy and Portugal — consumption exceeds 70 grams. For animal protein, however, the consumption pattern varies more from country to country. In the United States and Canada animal protein intake is about 65 grams per day, over two thirds of the total of all kinds of protein. In Italy and Portugal animal protein consumption averages only about 25 grams per day, little more than a third of the total (Figure 6–2).

It is difficult to forecast how far men will go in shifting their diets to more animal products. In North America, where average caloric intake has remained virtually unchanged over the past twenty years, animal protein consumption has risen by about a third — though recently the increase has apparently ceased. In Sweden, Norway and Switzerland, where the average person consumes fewer calories than before the war, animal protein intake appears to have been sta-

2. It is contended by some authorities, however, that full utilization of vegetable proteins, being dependent on careful dietary balance, is difficult to achieve. Recent research in nutrition, particularly in relation to the amino acids, has reopened many questions concerning dietary adequacy of various combinations of foodstuffs.

Figure 6–2. Per Capita Daily Consumption of Protein, by Source and Country, 1956–1957

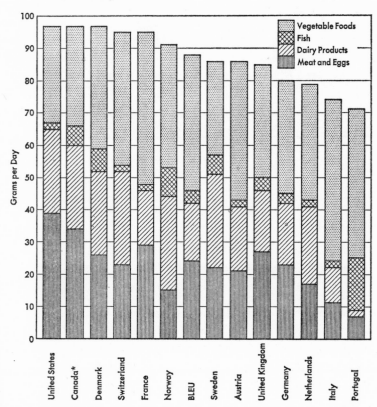

Source: OEEC, *Agricultural and Food Statistics,* Paris, 1959.
* 1956 only.

bilized at a level substantially below that in North America. Elsewhere a gradual rise in animal protein consumption, averaging 1 to 3 per cent annually, was recorded in recent years, with some indications of approaching stability (Table 6–2).

For the agricultural industry this question of future consumption of livestock products is of vast importance. If the desire for food in the form of livestock products stabilizes, the farmer faces a market which will expand at approximately the same rate as population.

Table 6–2. Daily Per Capita Consumption of Animal Protein, 1959, and Changes, 1952–1959, by Country

COUNTRY	AMOUNT (GRAMS) 1959	INDEX: 1952 = 100		
		1955	1957	1959
U. S.	66	105	108	108
Canada	64	107	103	107
Denmark	59	93	100	106
France	52	104	109	116
Sweden	52	93	93	91
U. K.	52	111	113	116
Switzerland	51	102	100	100
Norway	49	93	95	91
BLEU	47	102	107	112
Austria	46	110	116	121
Germany	46	110	118	118
Netherlands	45	108	108	113
Italy	27	110	120	129
Portugal	25	110	130	125

Source: OEEC, *General Statistics,* Paris, May 1961.

If, however, use of livestock products continues to grow — even at the expense of other foods, as has been the case in most of the North Atlantic region — the farmer faces a market which will grow more rapidly than population.[3] In this circumstance it is worth while to take a closer look at food consumption habits and changes in recent years.

Dairy Products

One of the "immutable truths" of nutritional and agricultural folklore appears to be in process of being discovered false. It has generally been believed that consumption of milk in one form or another rises rapidly as incomes rise (and as education spreads).

In most of the countries under consideration dairy products, measured in terms of milk equivalent, are being consumed in vir-

---

3. There are other factors at work here, of course, which affect the future market. One of the most important is the efficiency of livestock food production — the "feed-output ratio." Such changes are discussed later.

Table 6–3.   Per Capita Consumption of Fresh Milk, Cheese and Butter, by Country, Prewar and 1950s

(*Kilograms of Fresh Milk Equivalent*[a])

COUNTRY	PREWAR	1953–1955	1956–1958
Canada	474	402	391
U. S.	324	273	271
BLEU	292	370	350
France	265	289	324
Germany	344	325	330
Italy	116	149	156
Netherlands	(295)	312	325
Austria	295	293	292
Denmark	(350)	347	416
Norway	394	352	347
Portugal	27	41	42
Sweden	(480)	451	403
Switzerland	(440)	419	409
U. K.	368	323	350

Sources: OEEC, Paris, *Agricultural and Food Statistics,* 1959; and *Agriculture,* 1961. Estimates for prewar period, shown in parentheses, required to adjust discrepancies in two sources.

a. Based on 10 kg. per kg. of cheese and 19.2 kg. per kg. of butter.

tually stable or declining quantities, despite rapid rises in per capita income in all countries. Only in Belgium, France, Italy and Portugal (and perhaps Denmark and the Netherlands) is per capita consumption higher than it was in prewar years (Table 6–3).

Per capita consumption of fluid milk was increasing appreciably during the latter part of the 1950s in only a few of the northern countries.[4] Butter consumption in half the countries rose from 1953–1955 to 1956–1958, but in six markets the prewar levels of consumption had not been regained. In Canada, the United States, Norway, Sweden and the United Kingdom the decline was sharp.

Except where cheese consumption was already very high (as in

4. The increased use of all milk products in Denmark, shown in Table 6–3, reflects greater consumption of butter, a change nearly forced on the Danes as export markets failed to develop rapidly.

Sweden and Switzerland) at the beginning of the decade, consumption tended to rise during the 1950s. In all countries the prewar level was reached or exceeded.

As will be seen presently, this tendency toward stabilization or decline in demand for dairy products has far-reaching implications for the structure of agriculture in the future. Dairy farming, while it has become increasingly capital-intensive, is still the small farmer's stand-by, since it produces a regular flow of cash income. Without an expanding market many small producers will find themselves hard put to increase their incomes.

Meat, Poultry and Eggs

Per capita consumption of meat, poultry and eggs shows about as much national variation as consumption of milk and dairy products. To some extent, however, the variations offset each other. Thus, in the United States, where low cheese and butter consumption pulls the amount of milk used per person well below most other countries in the region, consumption of meat and eggs is high — 114 kilograms per person in 1959. In Sweden and Switzerland, where milk use is very high, consumption of meat and eggs is relatively low. In the United Kingdom and France, where milk consumption (and per capita income) is appreciably lower, use of meat and eggs is higher than in Sweden and Switzerland.

There is a wide variation in the national averages, intensified to an extent by this tendency in some countries to offset low consumption of one group of livestock products by high consumption of another. Against the American figure of 114 kilograms of meat and eggs per person in 1959, the average Portuguese had only 19 kilograms (though a good supply of fish helped to ease the difference a little). Canadians, Danes, Frenchmen and Britons consumed from 80 to 100 kilograms each of meat and eggs. Consumption exceeded 60 kilograms but fell short of 75 kilograms in all of the other countries except the Netherlands (56), Norway (45) and Italy (35).

Income and Consumption of Livestock Products

Despite variations in patterns of consumption, as well as widely differing price levels, the use of livestock products is fairly closely

Figure 6–3. Per Capita Consumption of All Livestock Products[a] Related to Per Capita Private Consumption Expenditures, by Country, 1959

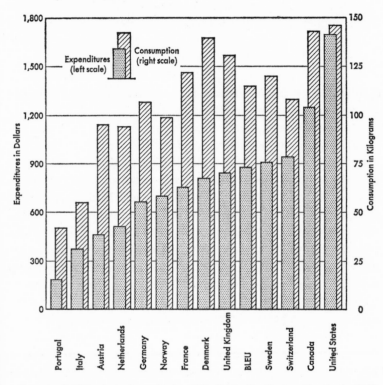

Sources: OEEC, *Agriculture,* Paris, 1959; FAO, *Production Yearbook, 1960,* Rome, 1961.

a. Actual weight of meat, fish and eggs plus 10 per cent of weight of milk consumed fresh or equivalent in butter and cheese. Dairy products data are averages for 1956–1958.

related to income differences. Figure 6–3 relates consumer expenditures in 1959 for all goods and services to the average consumption of livestock products (including, in this case, fish). The trend is fairly clear: as consumer expenditures rise the consumption of livestock products goes up as well. The curve is not smooth, the most notable exceptions being France and Denmark, on the side of high consumption of livestock products, though per capita incomes fall in the middle range, and Belgium, Sweden and Switzerland, on the low-consumption but high-income side. Nevertheless, the evidence is rather convincing in support of the point made at the beginning of this chapter: if they can afford it, people like their food converted from products of the soil to animals.

Cereals and Potatoes

If the outlook is for increased consumption of most livestock products, the opposite can be almost assuredly forecast for the historical food staples — cereals and potatoes.

Declining human consumption of cereals and potatoes in the North Atlantic region will continue a long-term trend (Figure 6–4). Records of human consumption of these products do not go back very far for most countries, but it is probably safe to say that in some of the northern European countries and North America the decline in per capita consumption was occurring in the last half of the nineteenth century. In others the turning point apparently came between the two world wars. Italy apparently has joined the majority with respect to decreasing cereals consumption but is steadily increasing its consumption of potatoes from a very low level — which means for many Italians an improved and diversified diet, as potatoes are being substituted for bread and pulses.

Differences in per capita consumption of cereals and of potatoes between the various countries of the region are enormous. In Italy the average person consumed about 140 kilograms of flour and rice in 1959, double the amount of the average North American, though potato consumption per person was roughly equal in the two areas. In Sweden cereals consumption was similar to and potato consumption about double that in America. Flour and rice consumption was between 80 and 100 kilograms per person annually in Belgium, Denmark, Germany, the Netherlands, Norway, Switzerland and the United Kingdom. However, Belgians and Germans consumed about 140 kilograms of potatoes, the Dutch, Norwegians, Swiss and British about 100 kilograms or less.[5]

Most important from an agricultural standpoint is the fact that nearly everywhere in Western Europe — but not in North America

5. FAO, *Production Yearbook, 1960,* Rome, 1961.

Figure 6–4. Annual Per Capita Consumption of Cereals and Potatoes, Selected Countries and Periods, 1910–1914 to 1959[a]

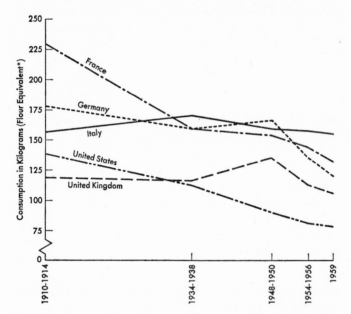

Sources: 1910–1914 — P. Lamartine Yates, *Food, Land and Manpower in Western Europe*, Macmillan, London, 1960; and U. S. Bureau of the Census, *Historical Statistics of the United States, Colonial Times to 1957*, Washington, 1960.

1934–1938 — OEEC, *Agricultural and Food Statistics*, Paris, 1959. Data for other periods from FAO, *Production Yearbook, 1960*, Rome, 1961.

a. Figure shown for BLEU for 1910–1914 is for Belgium only; figures shown for 1934–1938 for BLEU and the Netherlands are for 1936–1938 and those for Germany are for 1935–1938.

* Potatoes included at one fourth actual weight.

— human demand for these staple products has been falling more rapidly than population has been increasing. The total market for these products, in the form of food for direct human consumption, has been declining. With the prospect of only modest population growth in these countries and with the considerable decline in per capita consumption of cereals and potatoes which could occur before the low levels in North America are reached, this declining market may well continue. The implications of this for agriculture inside and outside Europe are discussed later.

Direct human consumption is, however, only part of the market for cereals and potatoes. In the European countries under consideration less than half the total cereals available in recent years — domestic production and net imports — have been used as flour (or in the manufacture of alcoholic beverages). Roughly the same proportion of potatoes is consumed directly by humans. Both products are important feeds for livestock. With the demand for livestock products expected to rise more rapidly than population, total demand for cereals (and temporarily for potatoes) will unquestionably be better than the prospective flour market indicates.

Sugar

Nearly all of the people of the North Atlantic region obtain about 10 to 15 per cent of their caloric intake from sugar. North Americans, Britons and Scandinavians eat the most sugar — 40 to 50 kilograms per person per year. The people of the Netherlands and Switzerland eat about 40 kilograms each, while those of Austria, Belgium, France and Germany consume only about two thirds as much sugar. In Italy and Portugal sugar remains a luxury, with per capita consumption about 20 kilograms a year.

Per capita consumption of sugar has been fairly stable in most countries in recent years. Notably British consumption has risen steadily to reach the highest level in the entire region — about 50 kilograms per person. In Scandinavia and North America use of sugar is apparently stable at a point somewhat lower than that in Britain. Elsewhere yearly increases have been modest.

While some differences may continue to exist in the average consumption of sugar in the various countries, it is probable that the levels in Belgium, France and Germany will be raised over the coming years close to those prevailing in most of the other countries. Consumption in Italy and Portugal will take longer to approach the levels in the other countries.

Fats and Oils

Fats and oils (including butter, discussed earlier) have approximately the same importance as sugar as a source of calories for the average person in the North Altantic region, though there are considerable national differences. In the Netherlands per capita consumption of 28 kilograms (fat content) per year in the mid–1950s provided 23 per cent of total caloric intake. At the other extreme fats and oils constituted only 13 per cent of total calories in France, Italy and Switzerland. Only in these countries and Portugal (and perhaps Denmark) does there appear any tendency in recent years for per capita consumption to rise. On the basis of experience there is little reason to predict that consumption of these foods will increase much faster than population in most countries, and in some — Denmark, Germany, the Netherlands and Norway — it is probable that per capita consumption will decline somewhat. If, as appears likely, butter and lard gain a more important place in consumption of fats and oils in a number of countries, the per capita use of vegetable fats may well decrease.

Fruits and Vegetables

Pleasing as they are from the standpoint of variety in the diet, fruits and vegetables (including pulses and nuts) make only a minor contribution to the average caloric intake for most people in the region. Nowhere do they account for as much as 10 per cent of the caloric value of the average diet and in some countries little more than half that proportion. They are, however, of considerable importance to the agricultural industry. Modest increases in per capita consumption over the coming years are likely.

LONG-TERM TRENDS

On the basis of the experience of the last decade it appears that per capita food consumption, measured in calories, is changing very little. However, the average diet in most countries is becoming qualitatively superior, measured in animal protein consumption.

In general, this trend is borne out by the rather meager long-term information available concerning food consumption. Data are available for a period of years before World War I for seven countries. In two of them — France and the United States — per capita consumption then considerably exceeded today's norm of about 3,000–3,100 calories. Since then average daily intake has fallen by roughly

Table 6–4.   Changes in Per Capita Food Consumption, Selected Foods and Countries, 1910–1914 to 1959

COMMODITY	U. S.	BEL-GIUM	FRANCE	GER-MANY	ITALY	SWITZER-LAND	U. K.
			INDEX (1910–1914 = 100)				
Cereals	54	67	58	67	95	81	88
Potatoes	51	69	57	70	191	57	91
Sugar	115	224	205	154	434	173	141
Fats	115	142	94	136	138	...	190
Meat	} 117	200	220	112	154	100	118
Fish		...	...	90	143	143	52
Liquid Milk	} 128	144	94	89	136	70	209
Cheese		...	191	186	149	73	110
Eggs	(118)	221	138	200	125	137	201

Sources: P. Lamartine Yates, *Food, Land and Manpower in Western Europe,* Macmillan, London, 1960; FAO, *Production Yearbook, 1960,* Rome, 1961; OEEC, *Agriculture,* Paris, 1961; USDA, *Agricultural Statistics, 1957* and *1960,* Washington, 1958 and 1961.

10 per cent in the United States and about 15 per cent in France. In Germany and Switzerland the average consumption in the earlier period was about 3,100 calories daily, roughly equal to present levels. In Italy and the United Kingdom, where consumption was well below the 3,100 calorie level, and in Belgium, where it was somewhat below that level, the trend has been upward. In the United Kingdom the 3,100 level has been reached and exceeded.

In these seven countries, with the exception of Switzerland, livestock products have comprised a larger part of the diet in recent years than in the period before World War I (Table 6–4). Potato consumption has fallen in all of them except Italy, where potatoes have been a comparative luxury, particularly in the southern part of the country. Cereals are no longer consumed in such great quantities, though the declines in Italy, Switzerland and the United Kingdom have not been great. Meat and egg consumption is generally higher in recent years. In countries where milk consumption was low in earlier years — Italy, Belgium and the United Kingdom — it has tended to rise, but it has fallen somewhat in Switzerland, Germany and France.

In general it is fair to say that over the past half century there has been a tendency for diets in the North Atlantic countries to become more similar. Averages appear to be converging at a caloric level of about 3,000 to 3,200 calories per person per day, with the proportion derived from livestock products moving up toward what appears to be a maximum of about 45 per cent. Vegetable fats and sugar have gradually replaced part of the declining consumption of cereals and potatoes. Exceptions to this generalization appear to be mainly related to the level of per capita income in the various countries.

EXPENDITURES FOR FOOD

In recent years increases in consumer expenditures for food have been much greater than increases in quantities of food consumed. In most countries only a minor part of such increases in expenditures has been due to higher prices paid to farmers. Most of the increases in consumer outlays for food are attributable to larger purchases of the more expensive kinds of food and to higher costs of food processing and marketing.

Total expenditures for food in the fifteen countries under consideration rose from $80 billion in 1950 to $140 billion in 1960.[6] Measured in constant (1954) prices the increase was from $95 billion to $125 billion, or over 30 per cent.

There are wide variations in the per capita expenditures in the various countries. In 1955 they ranged from $81 in Portugal to $361 in the United States (in 1954 prices). The average for the EEC countries was $173 and for the EFTA countries $192. In North America food purchases took about 23 per cent of all consumer outlays, in Europe about 34 per cent.[7]

A very rough gauge of the relationship between "quality" of diets and cost is shown in Table 6–5. In column 1 the countries for which information is available have been ranked in terms of the number of grams of animal protein for each thousand calories in the

6. Figures, calculated at official exchange rates prevailing in 1954, are for the OEEC countries and the United States and Canada. OEEC, *General Statistics,* Paris, January and March 1961.

7. OEEC, *General Statistics,* Paris, January, July and September 1961; and J. Frederic Dewhurst, John O. Coppock and Paul Lamartine Yates, *Europe's Needs and Resources,* Twentieth Century Fund, New York, 1961.

Table 6–5.   Comparative Per Capita Expenditures for Food Related to Animal Protein Content of Units of Food, Selected Countries, Annual Average, 1948–1950 to 1959

COUNTRY	ANIMAL PROTEIN PER 1,000 CALORIES			ANNUAL EXPENDITURES PER 1,000 CALORIES OF FOOD PER DAY[a]		
	AMOUNT (GRAMS)	INDEX: (1948–1950 = 100)		AMOUNT	INDEX: (1950 = 100)	
	1959	1954–1956	1959	1959	1955	1959
	(1)	(2)	(3)	(4)	(5)	(6)
U. S.	21.1	109	110	$117	103	105
Canada	20.3	109	111	86	108	114
Sweden	17.8	107	107	78	105	115
Denmark	17.7	92	96	58	94	102
France	17.7	114	124	68[b]	114	118
Norway	16.4	92	96	64	99	111
BLEU	16.0	113	122	85[c]	107[c]	118[c]
Germany	15.9	123	136	67	125	154
U. K.	15.8	106	110	69	102	106
Austria	15.6	129	139	54	118	155
Netherlands	15.2	110	114	50	109	116
Italy	10.0	111	123	58	109	116

Sources: FAO, *Production Yearbook, 1960,* Rome, 1961; OEEC, *General Statistics,* Paris, January, July and September 1961; 1955 expenditures for Germany derived from J. Frederic Dewhurst, John O. Coppock, P. Lamartine Yates and Associates, *Europe's Needs and Resources,* The Twentieth Century Fund, New York, 1961.
   a. At 1954 prices.   b. At 1959 exchange rate.   c. Belgium only.

average daily diet. Column 4 of the table shows the annual average expenditure of consumers to obtain 1,000 calories daily. Of the twelve countries, the expenditure rankings of only Denmark, Belgium-Luxembourg and Italy are seriously out of place in relation to the rankings by amount of animal protein in the average diet.[8] The

8. The Norwegians and the Danes obtain a considerable amount of animal protein from fish, a relatively cheap source. In recent years fish provided about 15 per cent of all animal protein in Norway, about 12 per cent in Denmark.

index numbers show the increase in costs (measured in constant prices) as the volume of animal protein per thousand calories rose in all countries but Denmark and Norway in the 1950s. For most countries the rise in expenditures closely parallels the increase in the percentage of the diet composed of animal protein.

In the latter half of the 1950s there was a marked tendency in a number of countries for the animal protein content per unit of food consumed to rise at a much slower rate than in earlier years. In all countries with a high-protein diet (except France) the increases from 1955 to 1959 were nominal or represented returns in the direction of the higher levels of the beginning of the decade. In those countries lower down the dietary scale, diets continued to shift in the direction of more animal protein but (except in Italy) at a more leisurely rate.

COMPARATIVE VOLUME OF FOOD CONSUMPTION

The discussion above has been in terms of the consumption of food as measured by specific commodities, the chief nutrients and expenditures. None of these measures is entirely adequate for the purposes required in this study. Some measure of total food consumption per person is needed to supplement the comparisons of caloric and protein availabilities and expenditures for food.

The Committee on Agricultural Problems of the Economic Commission for Europe, in cooperation with the FAO, has constructed a volume index of food consumption.[9] This index, in a slightly modified form, has been used here to measure changes in the volume of per capita food consumption in each country during the 1950s.[10]

9. ECE/FAO, *European Agriculture in 1965,* Document AGRI/167, Geneva, 1960, Annex II, p. 29, mimeo.

10. See Appendix III for details of this index. The principal modifications in the ECE/FAO index were the additions of fats (other than butter), fruits, vegetables and pulses to the items covered by the committee. Fish is excluded. The index generally reflects prices paid to producers in Europe. If North American prices were used the differences in volume between the United States and Canada on the one hand and the European countries on the other would be somewhat reduced.

Table 6–6. Volume Indexes of Per Capita Food Consumption, Selected Periods, Prewar to 1959   (*U. S. = 100*)

REGION OR COUNTRY	PREWAR	1947– 1949	1950– 1952	1953– 1955	1956– 1957	1959
U. S.	100	100	100	100	100	100
Canada	95	98	96	98	97ᵃ	96
EEC	75	60	69	72	73	74
BLEU	79	74	79	81	81	80
France	87	79	85	88	88	88
Germany	85	54	70	75	77	77
Italy	53	44	51	53	55	57
Netherlands	78	64	69	70	70	73
EFTA	87	73	75	78	80	81
Austria	81	54	67	72	75	76
Denmark	101	89	83	85	89	89
Norway	78	68	71	71	70	72
Portugal	44	43	45	45	45	43
Sweden	87	81	83	80	80	77
Switzerland	94	81	84	82	85	81
U. K.	93	78	79	84	86	88

Sources: OEEC, *Agricultural and Food Statistics*, Paris, 1959; FAO, *Production Yearbook, 1960*, Rome, 1961; and note on method in Appendix III.
   a. 1956 only.

The country indexes are shown in Table 6–6 in comparison to the United States. Most of the European countries show average food consumption per person, as measured by this index, at about 75 to 90 per cent of American volume. Only in Portugal and Italy is the volume substantially below this range. Denmark, France and Britain stand at the top in Western Europe, consuming about 90 per cent of the American volume. Norway and Sweden rank much lower, but both would be raised considerably in the scale if fish were included in the index (a factor which would also greatly improve the very low ranking of Portugal). Most of the countries show a tendency toward approaching the American rate, but some appear stalled, at least temporarily, at only about 75 to 80 per cent of the volume.

Table 6–7. Volume Indexes of Per Capita Food Consumption, by Country, Prewar to 1959   (*1950–1952 = 100*)

REGION OR COUNTRY	PREWAR	1947– 1949	1950– 1952	1953– 1955	1956– 1957	1959
Canada	91	102	100	105	105ᵃ	106
U. S.	92	100	100	103	104	106
EEC	100	87	100	107	110	115
BLEU	91	94	100	105	106	107
France	94	92	100	106	107	110
Germany	112	78	100	109	115	116
Italy	96	87	100	107	112	120
Netherlands	103	92	100	104	105	112
EFTA	107	98	100	107	111	114
Austria	112	81	100	110	116	120
Denmark	113	107	100	105	111	114
Norway	101	96	100	103	103	108
Portugal	89	96	100	103	104	101
Sweden	97	99	100	100	101	99
Switzerland	104	97	100	101	106	103
U. K.	109	99	100	109	114	119

Sources: OEEC, *Agricultural and Food Statistics,* Paris, 1959; FAO, *Production Yearbook, 1960,* Rome, 1961; and Appendix III for method of computing index.
a. 1956 only.

Recent Trends

Rationing of food in the countries of Western Europe was being progressively eliminated from about 1948 on and had virtually disappeared by 1952. As Table 6–6 indicates, the volume of consumption gained relative to the North American volume in most countries in which rationing had been the least stringent and had ended earlier. It is of interest to note, however, that by 1959 the volume of food consumption in the European countries had not yet come as near to parity with Canada and the United States as it had been in the last years before World War II. The Common Market countries taken together had almost reached the prewar position relative to North American consumption, as a result of relative improvements in Italy and France. Elsewhere, however, the gap between the North American and the European volume of food consumption had widened.

Table 6–7 shows that full recovery of the prewar level of consumption came over a wide time range in European countries. It was achieved rapidly in Belgium, Portugal and Sweden, but not until 1959 in Denmark (which had by far the highest level of food consumption in Europe in the prewar period).

After about 1951 the rise in per capita consumption was at first rapid (about 3.5 per cent annually), then changed quite suddenly to a much slower expansion of less than 1.5 per cent per year in Europe. Only in Italy did consumption increase at more than 2 per cent per year after 1953–1955. In North America the expansion throughout the 1950s averaged about 0.75 per cent.

It was this abrupt slowing in the rate of growth of per capita food consumption in Europe, long before the North American volume had been reached, which led to the great reappraisal of agricultural prospects in the North Atlantic region. It is the prospect of demand rising only slowly which puts force behind the demands of farmers and their spokesmen in Europe for strengthening the protectionist and autarkic characteristics of agricultural policies, whether national or agreed to by several governments. It is this fact which will immensely complicate any effort to restore "economy" to production and trade in food products.

7

Growth of the Market

On a global basis there is no serious difficulty in predicting what the market for food will be. Except for the relatively minor dislocations caused by withholding of food from the market (as the United States and Canada have done in recent years), consumption will equal output. Nearly all the food produced in the world is consumed in the same or the following year. The dire predictions concerning the world's food supply are based on the presumed inability of world agriculture to keep up with the minimum nutritional demands of the world's population. So far the prophets of doom, from Malthus through Marx to the neo-Malthusians, have been proved only partially correct. Food supply per person has not declined (except for limited periods, as in China recently).

This global analysis has relatively little to do with the problems with which this study is concerned. Here we are dealing with the problems of industrialized countries accustomed to a considerable volume of international trade in foods — with the seventh of the world's population which, despite a recent record of agricultural protectionism on national lines, is not dependent on the equation that consumption will automatically equal national output.

In 1955 there were about 432 million people in the fifteen countries grouped here in the North Atlantic region. By 1960 that number had risen to 460 million. By 1970 it will probably be about 515 million and by 1980 about 575 million. In 1955 about 40 per cent of the total population was in North America; by 1980 Canada and the United States will have almost half the total. Economically capable of exercising choice, what foods are these people likely to demand?[1]

FUTURE FOOD DEMAND

As discussed in Chapter 6, recent trends in food consumption can be summarized rather simply: per capita use of cereals and potatoes declined throughout the North Atlantic region in the 1950s, continuing a trend of more than half a century in most countries. This reduction was offset by rising consumption of livestock products, vegetable fats and — to less extent — sugar. However, the pattern of consumption of the various livestock products appeared to be changing. In a number of countries fluid milk consumption apparently passed a peak, but in some countries more milk was being consumed as cheese and, more recently, as butter. Nearly everywhere the per capita consumption of meat and eggs continued to rise.

In very few countries of the region, however, was total per capita food consumption — measured by the number of calories in the foods available at the retail level — rising. Essentially the general pattern throughout the region was one of substitution of expensive foods for cheaper foods, as indicated by the rise in expenditures per thousand calories of food per day, shown in Table 6–5.

Most analysts agree that this pattern of substitution which has marked the last few years will continue. They tend to disagree only as to the rate of substitution. Behind such disagreement is a mass of conflicting data with respect to the effects of prices, incomes and habits on the demand for particular foods.

1. As late as 1952 the FAO was establishing, even for the highly developed countries, "consumption targets" designed to assure nutritional adequacy, on the assumption that limited supplies of food would be available. They appear to have been made largely without belief that some markets for food were approaching something like saturation. See FAO, *Second World Food Survey*, Rome, 1952. For an analysis of the targets in comparison to results, see P. Lamartine Yates, *Food, Land and Manpower in Western Europe*, Macmillan, London, 1960, Chap. 3.

Price Elasticity

The area in which there is probably the most agreement among agricultural analysts is the effect of price changes on the demand for food. The prevailing view is that even over fairly long periods of time changes in the price of foodstuffs in general in relation to other prices have little effect on the total volume of food purchased per person. Thus the "price elasticity" for food in general is low: a considerable reduction or increase in the price of foodstuffs will not result in a proportionate change in per capita food consumption.

However, changes in the prices of particular foods in relation to the prices of other foods will shift consumers from one kind of food to another. Moreover, the more physical similarity there is between two foodstuffs whose prices diverge the greater is the price elasticity. Thus a reduction in bread prices relative to meat prices will bring only a limited shift in the direction of more bread consumption.[2] However, a rise in the price of butter in relation to that of margarine (particularly if the latter is similar to butter in color and packaging) will have immediate and very great effect on the consumption of each of the two products.

Thus, while relative price changes for foodstuffs in general do not have much impact on the volume of consumption, price elasticities for individual foods may be considerable. For agriculture as an industry this apparent fact is simultaneously reassuring and ominous. The industry as a whole is secure in the knowledge that, within a rather broad range and over a considerable time period, changing prices of food will not have much effect on the volume of sales. For an individual producer, however, a price change for an acceptable substitute for the product in which he specializes can have immediate and far-reaching effects. And if the relative price change results from a technological development rather than from a fortuitous circumstance, such as unusual weather conditions, adjustment to the new situation may be painful for many producers. A

2. In fact such a reduction might be accompanied by no increase in consumption at all, because of the long-term trend away from bread and the related trend toward livestock products, a trend which is, however, responsive to factors other than price changes.

recent case in point is the rapid development in the production, feeding and marketing of broiler chickens. Between 1949 and 1958 production of "commercial broilers" — those produced in "factories" — in the United States rose from almost 1.1 billion pounds to 3.9 billion pounds. During the same period farm and "backyard" chicken production (for sale) fell from 1.9 billion pounds to 1.1 billion pounds. Thus total chicken marketings rose by two thirds, but "chicken farmers" had much less of the larger market. Prices of chickens fell by a quarter to a third[3] and per capita consumption rose by nearly 45 per cent. During the same period total meat consumption rose by only 7.4 pounds per person per year — about 5 per cent. Per capita consumption of pork, chicken's nearest competitor, fell over the period by more than 10 per cent — with prices rising by 6 to 8 per cent.

Income Elasticity[4]

In addition to price elasticity and its effect on food consumption, another concept is widely used in forecasting demand. In a changing economy "income elasticity" of demand for food must also be taken into account. Income elasticity relates expenditures for particular items of consumption to changes in disposable income. Ordinarily, income elasticity of demand is determined by analyzing a period of time during which incomes have changed. However, analyses are also made of expenditures during the same period for particular goods by persons in different income brackets. Periodically daring analysts attempt to estimate income elasticity of demand on an international basis: when the average income of Country B reaches the average income of Country A, the demand for Commodity X in Country B should be so much. If this sort of analysis is to mean anything, the "so much" to be spent by persons in Country B for Commodity X must be close to that spent in Country A in the earlier year.

---

3. Wholesale prices, New York, chickens of three pounds or more dressed weight. USDA, *Agricultural Statistics, 1959,* Washington, p. 424. Other information in this section drawn entirely from *ibid.*, pp. 411–23.

4. The analysis in this section is actually in terms of "expenditure elasticity," which differs from "income elasticity" by the exclusion of personal savings.

How far the "so much" deviates from the exact figure for Country A depends on such factors as the analysts can isolate which would logically bring about a different result in Country B.

Such analysis is hazardous at best within a single, reasonably homogeneous society. It is increasingly dangerous when applied to different societies. It is peculiarly subject to error when applied to food demand, for two reasons.

First, habit has a strong influence over food consumption. A sudden rise in an Italian's disposable income is unlikely to reduce his bread and *pasta* consumption to the level of a compatriot who has enjoyed the higher income for most of his life. Still less is it likely to influence him to consume as much milk as a Norwegian with the same income. Changes in habits of food consumption are unquestionably related to income changes, but they are far from immediately and automatically related. For example, in the United Kingdom, the most urbanized and one of the wealthiest of the nations of Western Europe, potato consumption dropped steadily until World War II. Difficulties encountered during the war years in obtaining food supplies from abroad made the British much more dependent on their own production. Potatoes grow well in Britain and production was easily and greatly expanded. Amid much grumbling, per capita potato consumption rose rapidly above the 80 kilograms per year eaten just before the war to about 120 kilograms. This was more than per capita consumption in the latter part of the nineteenth century. After World War II British incomes recovered rapidly and rose to unprecedented levels during the 1950s. By the middle years of the decade there were few limitations on food imports and more people than ever had the money to buy what they wished. Yet in 1959 the average Briton ate over 90 kilograms of potatoes, much more than in the prewar years and nearly as much as in the period just before World War I. Several years of "conditioning" had been sufficient to set the food habits of a large number of people whose growing incomes would normally have been accompanied by a much lower level of potato consumption.

The second major difficulty in relating food consumption to income levels has to do with changing marketing methods. Nearly all foods are processed in some form before they reach the retail level.

As incomes rise most persons appear to be willing to spend more money at the store, but the additional expenditure is split between more or better quality foods and more processing. Bread comes sliced and wrapped, fruits and vegetables are canned or frozen, more milk is pasteurized or turned into manufactured products.

In the years immediately after World War II farmers in the United States received almost exactly half of what consumers spent for food in retail stores. Although retail food prices over the next several years rose at about the same rate as other prices and per capita consumption of food in general remained about stable, by the late 1950s farmers received less than 40 per cent of consumer expenditures for food. Thus income elasticity as it applies to consumer expenditures for food is not a very useful indicator of the prospective volume of food sales or "farm gate demand."

Comparative Elasticities

It is possible to construct a record of income (or, more properly, expenditure) elasticities for food for most of the countries covered in this study for recent years. Unfortunately, the results are a hodgepodge of conflicting evidence.

Where all per capita private consumption expenditures are high and food expenditures take a relatively small proportion of total spending, there is reason to assume that expenditure elasticities (based on constant prices) for food will be relatively low. Table 7–1 describes this hypothetical situation (since it is based on constant prices) during the 1950s. The results are far from consistent. In Canada the elasticity was about 0.9 (i.e., for every 10 per cent rise in per capita consumption expenditures as a whole, there was a 9 per cent rise in expenditures for food), while in the United States the elasticity was only about 0.5. Expenditures for food (in constant prices) in both countries were less than a quarter of all private expenditures.

In a second group of European countries with relatively high per capita consumption expenditures and with food representing a quarter to a third of that outlay the record is quite mixed. The elasticities (in constant prices) for the four countries with per capita expenditures totaling more than $600 ranged from 1.4 in Belgium

Table 7–1. Per Capita Private Consumption Expenditures at
1954 Prices, Total and for Food, 1950, and Expenditure
Elasticity for Food, by Country, 1950–1959

	TOTAL		FOR FOOD		
COUNTRY	1950	PERCENTAGE INCREASE, 1950– 1959	AS PER CENT OF TOTAL, 1950	PERCENT- AGE IN- CREASE, 1950– 1959	EXPENDI- TURE ELAS- TICITY
Canada	$1,006	15.9	23.5	14.3	0.9
U. S.	1,414	13.7	24.1	7.1	0.5
EEC					
Belgium	726	13.6	28.7	18.7	1.4
France	501	33.3	36.9	21.3	0.6
Germany	351	69.8	(33.9)	(62.0)	(0.9)
Italy	249	39.2	47.5	34.4	0.9
Netherlands	383	19.5	33.0	15.5	0.8
EFTA					
Austria	280	50.7	38.2	47.7	0.9
Denmark	613	16.5	30.0	4.1	0.2
Norway	543	15.0	32.7	6.1	0.4
Portugal[a]	154[a]	20.7[b]	53.5[a]	5.1[b]	0.2
Sweden	663	18.6	31.6	4.1	0.2
U. K.	625	17.7	32.5	11.1	0.6

Sources: Derived from OEEC, *General Statistics,* Paris, January and March 1961.
a. 1952.   b. 1952–1957.

to 0.6 in the United Kingdom on down to 0.2 in Sweden and Denmark. In all four of these countries, as in the United States and
Canada, total per capita consumer expenditures rose at a relatively modest rate during this period, less than 20 percent. Norway
and the Netherlands, similar to these four countries in terms of the
rates of increase of total per capita expenditures and the percentages spent for food, but with somewhat lower expenditures per
capita, had elasticities of 0.4 and 0.8, respectively. France, Germany, Austria and Italy had rapid rates of growth in total personal
expenditures per capita and in general higher proportions of income
were spent for food than in other countries. The elasticity for France

was 0.6, for the others 0.9. Portugal, poor and with a modest rate of growth, showed an elasticity of only 0.2.

This, of course, is a hypothetical situation based on constant prices. Prices did change considerably over the 1950s and not always consistently with respect to food and other consumption items. Table 7–2 is identical to Table 7–1 except that it is expressed in current prices. Here the range of expenditure elasticities narrows sharply. All fall between 0.7 and 1.0, with the exception of the 1.2 elasticity for the United Kingdom, which experienced the most radical increase in food prices in comparison to other prices.

On the face of it, the consistent pattern of expenditure elasticities shown in Table 7–2 does not prove much. Rich and poor countries, with widely different rates of growth, different rates of price inflation and different experiences with respect to relative changes in food prices and other prices, are scattered almost at random over the range of expenditure elasticities. There were six countries in which the volume (expenditures at constant prices) of food purchases increased by 11 per cent or less from 1950 to 1959. The United States and Portugal — the richest and poorest of the countries under consideration — shared a food expenditure elasticity at current prices of 0.7; food prices in the United States rose less rapidly than other prices, while the reverse was true in Portugal. The other four — Denmark, Norway, Sweden and the United Kingdom — had elasticities at current prices from 0.8 to 1.2. They shared one thing in common, however; food prices in all of them rose more than other prices. And in all six countries the rate of growth of total consumer expenditures (measured in constant prices) was relatively modest.

In the next group of countries — those with increases in volume of food expenditures (constant prices) ranging from 14 to 21 per cent — almost the entire range of elasticities at current prices was represented: France 0.7, Canada 0.8, the Netherlands 0.9 and Belgium 1.0. In the Netherlands food prices increased more rapidly than other prices; the reverse was true in the other three countries. Belgium had the lowest rate of growth in per capita consumer expenditures in the North Atlantic region, measured at constant prices; France had a high rate.

Table 7-2. Per Capita Private Consumption Expenditures at Current Prices, Total and for Food, 1950, and Expenditure Elasticity for Food, by Country, 1950–1959

COUNTRY	TOTAL		FOR FOOD		
	1950	PERCENT-AGE IN-CREASE, 1950–1959	AS PER CENT OF TOTAL, 1950	PERCENT-AGE IN-CREASE, 1950–1959	EXPENDI-TURE ELAS-TICITY
Canada	$ 877	45.5	24.8	34.4	0.8
U. S.	1,273	36.9	24.3	23.9	0.7
EEC					
Belgium	654	34.6	29.5	34.4	1.0
France	457ᵃ	130.8	39.0	90.1	0.7
Germany	315	110.0	(33.5)	(113.2)	(1.0)
Italy	214	73.1	49.4	58.1	0.8
Netherlands	459	54.0	32.7	50.6	0.9
EFTA					
Austria	202	128.7	38.3	113.7	0.9
Denmark	538	50.3	28.7	38.3	0.8
Norway	424	64.4	29.9	64.2	1.0
Portugal	148ᵇ	20.7ᶜ	51.7	13.6	0.7
Sweden	533	70.5	29.5	58.2	0.8
U. K.	521	61.4	29.1	71.0	1.2

Sources: Derived from OEEC, *General Statistics,* Paris, January and March, 1961.

a. At 350 francs per dollar.   b. 1952.   c. 1952–1957.

Italy had a food expenditure elasticity (based on current prices) of 0.8, Austria 0.9 and Germany 1.0. All three were in poor economic condition at the start of the period and all showed very rapid growth rates. Food prices rose more rapidly than other prices in Germany, less rapidly in the other two countries.

About all that can be drawn from these figures is the generalization that they support, in a rough manner, the view that a change in the relative price of food has comparatively little influence on the expenditure pattern of incremental income. Relative price declines in North America and Belgium evoked roughly the same response in this respect as did relative price increases in Scandinavia and the Netherlands.[5]

At the same time, these figures raise a rather serious doubt as to the usefulness of the experience in the 1950s in determining trends in expenditure elasticities for food. It is generally contended that as total expenditures rise the proportion spent for food declines, assuming reasonably stable relations between prices for food and other items. Indeed, this must have been true at some time in the past to explain the fact that in rich countries the proportion of income spent for food is smaller than in poor countries. The contention is not well supported by the elasticities shown in the last column of either Table 7–1 or Table 7–2.

What is in doubt here is not the validity of this contention as such. The question really is the validity of the constant-price indexes underlying the calculation of expenditures. It is a commonplace that the degree of processing which food undergoes before it reaches the retailer is increasing rapidly and radically — so much so that it can be said that in many instances the consumer today is not buying the same article he did a few years ago.

The final column in Table 7–3 shows the volume of food consumed (or available at retail) per capita in 1959 compared with the annual average in 1950–1952. In no country does the increase in expenditures calculated at constant prices match closely the increase in the physical volume of food consumed. While the weighting system on which this calculation of physical volume is based (see Appendix III) may not be infallible when applied to individual countries, the error is probably comparatively small.

5. Only in the United Kingdom would it appear that a sharp rise in food prices relative to other prices had an unmistakable influence on the use pattern of incremental per capita income. This is in part due to the choice of 1950 as the base year for the calculation, a year when rationing was still in force in England and retail prices were both subsidized and strictly controlled. If 1952, when most rationing and price controls had been lifted, is used as a base year, the increase in food prices relative to other prices resembles that in the Scandinavian countries; the expenditure elasticity for food at current prices, shown as 1.2 on Table 7–2, becomes 1.0.

Table 7–3. Indicators of Changes in Value and Volume of Per Capita Food Consumption, by Country, 1950–1959

COUNTRY	PER CENT OF PRIVATE CONSUMPTION EXPENDITURES SPENT FOR FOOD[a]		ANNUAL PERCENTAGE INCREASE IN PER CAPITA FOOD EXPENDITURES, 1950–1959		ANNUAL PERCENTAGE INCREASE IN VOLUME OF PER CAPITA FOOD CONSUMPTION
	1950	1959	CURRENT PRICES	CONSTANT PRICES	1950–1952 TO 1959
Canada	24	23	3.3	1.5	0.7
U. S.	24	23	2.4	0.7	0.7
EEC					
Belgium	29	30	3.3	2.0	0.8
France	37	34	7.4	2.1	1.2
Germany	(34)	(32)	(8.8)	(5.5)	1.9
Italy	48	46	5.2	3.3	2.3
Netherlands	33	32	4.7	1.7	1.3
EFTA					
Austria	38	38	8.8	4.5	2.3
Denmark	30	27	3.6	0.4	1.7
Norway	33	30	5.7	0.6	1.0
Portugal	54[b]	47[c]	2.7[d]	1.2[d]	0.1
Sweden	32	28	5.2	0.4	−0.1
U. K.	33	31	6.1	1.2	2.2

Sources: Tables 7–1, 7–2 and 6–7; and OEEC, *General Statistics*, Paris, January, July and September 1961.
a. At 1954 prices.   b. 1952.   c. 1957.   d. 1952–1957.

CONSUMPTION TRENDS AND PROJECTIONS

Because the reliability of estimates of consumer food expenditures at constant prices is apparently not a very good reflection of the physical requirement for food "at the farm gate" — of primary interest in this study — we have attempted a simpler — though perhaps no less "scientific" — technique for estimating future food demand. For lack of a better term, it may be called a "dietary convergence assumption." It has been noted in the preceding chapter that diets within the region have gradually become more similar, though very considerable differences remain.

Essentially this hypothesis concerning future food demand is based on a number of trends which have some historical statistical support, considerably more than is available for an analysis based on expenditure elasticities.[6] These trends are simple to identify. Very briefly, they indicate the following:

1. As countries in the North Atlantic region have become mainly urbanized, the average intake of food (food available at the retail level, including food consumed by farm families which has not entered the market) has tended to stabilize at 3,000 to 3,200 calories per person per day.

2. Improved incomes under these circumstances have tended to be used to purchase foods which are more highly processed and contain more animal protein. In addition, where climatic conditions limit local production of particular products, such as fruits and vegetables, people have been willing to spend more for these items brought from distant areas at high cost.[7]

3. Though the eating habits of individuals have changed relatively slowly, greater urbanization and higher incomes have resulted in more "eating out" and more access to foods brought from a distance. This has tended to speed the rate of change in eating habits. Nevertheless, rapid changes in dietary patterns are not likely to occur on a scale which would seriously affect estimates of future food consumption which are otherwise soundly based.

4. Populations which have already reached the average level of 3,000 to 3,200 calories and which include an increasing proportion of elderly people are likely to experience a decline in average food consumption (measured in calories) as the older population becomes proportionately more important.

5. In the North Atlantic region over the next two decades average personal incomes are likely to rise to a level in nearly every

6. There is no intention here of denying that "the rich eat more — or better — than the poor." They quite obviously do; better incomes are associated with better diets in all sample surveys undertaken. What is lacking is a convincing set of statistics to indicate how quickly people who become relatively affluent change their eating habits.

7. The same is true of various tropical products, which are outside the scope of this discussion.

country which will permit most people to buy the foods — in quantity and in kind — they most want. Shortage of income, while admittedly important in individual cases, is not likely to be statistically very important in determining the amount or the kinds of food people will purchase. Higher incomes will provide an impetus toward the greater purchase of expensive foods; habit will act as a brake on this tendency.

On the basis of these considerations it is estimated here that average food consumption in the North Atlantic region will increase only modestly in the next few years. The caloric value of all foods available at retail for each person will probably drop somewhat in some countries (though it will be slightly higher in the EEC countries other than Italy and substantially higher in Italy and Portugal). However, because the average person will be eating a somewhat different diet in 1970 and 1980, the "volume" of food per person (as measured by the farmer) will rise somewhat. In North America it will increase perhaps 1 per cent by 1970 and 4 per cent by 1980, with lower average caloric intake nearly offsetting the effect of changed diets. In Western Europe, however, the rise from 1955 will be about 9 per cent by 1970 and over 20 per cent by 1980.

Added to this will be the increase in demand resulting from population expansion. In Western Europe population will probably increase by only about 17 per cent between 1955 and 1980. In North America, however, the rise is likely to be about 53 per cent. (See Appendix I.) The result of all this will be an increase over 1955 in demand for food "at the farm gate" of about 30 per cent by 1970 and 60 per cent by 1980 in North America and about 20 per cent in 1970 and 40 per cent more in 1980 in Western Europe.

Projections of Dietary Composition

Predicting demand for particular foods is of course very hazardous. Nevertheless, there is some evidential support for detailed projections. The great stability of per capita food purchasing patterns in the United States over the past decade indicates that there is probably something like an "optimum diet" which puts at least temporary limits to changes in food purchasing patterns in societies in which a large part of the population can afford to buy the kinds of food they want. This is not to say that the optimum diet would be the same in all societies. Habit, availability, prices, climate, age structure of the population and many other factors would make for differences in diets. Nevertheless, in a region in which the flow of foodstuffs is relatively uninhibited there is probably a tendency for diets to become more rather than less similar.

As noted in the preceding chapter, the long-term trend in the region is away from cereals and potatoes in the direction of more sugar, meat, eggs and (until recently) dairy products. In those countries in which average caloric intake has increased, the same pattern of change in types of food has occurred as in countries in which caloric intake has fallen. In general, however, the decline in consumption of cereals and potatoes has been somewhat slower in the first group of countries.

In choosing the diets on which to make the forecast of food requirements in 1970 and 1980 it was necessary to take account of a "caloric ceiling," a trend toward more animal protein and a greater availability of processed fruits and vegetables (in Europe) in countries where such items must be imported. It was also necessary to make assumptions with respect to future price relations, particularly between prices of vegetable fats and oils and butter. Beyond these considerations it was necessary to take account of some national "habits" and for Portugal and Italy it was necessary to adjust for relatively low incomes.

The resultant projections are shown in Figure 7–1. It is expected that virtually the entire increase in per capita consumption will be in the form of livestock products, though a rise in per capita consumption of fruits and vegetables will more than offset declines in cereals and potatoes, notably in Canada, Austria, the Netherlands and Sweden. (See Appendix III, Tables A and C.)[8]

If these levels of consumption are achieved, they will constitute a very considerable improvement in the average diet in most countries in Western Europe, particularly in the EEC countries and in Austria and Portugal. Measured in terms of animal protein, how-

8. The reader should note that in Appendix III, Tables A and C, the quantities of food available are given in kilograms of actual weight. In Table D, however, the amount of food available is given in kilograms of "wheat equivalent." See the text of Appendix III.

Figure 7–1. Projected Changes in Annual Per Capita Food Consumption, North Atlantic Areas, 1954–1956 to 1970 and 1980

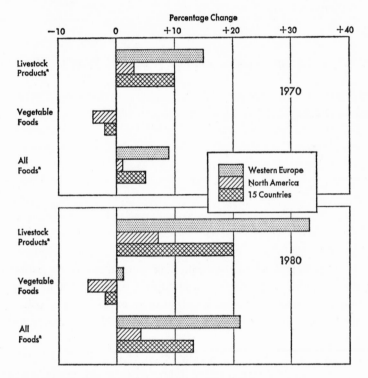

Sources: Derived from Appendix I and Appendix III, Tables A and C.
a. Excludes fish and marine oils.

ever, diets in most countries in Europe will still fall short of the level already achieved in Canada and the United States.

How is this expanded market for food to be supplied? The following chapters show how the market has been supplied in recent years of rapid growth. From this experience it will be seen that supplying an increase in the volume of food consumption of about 50 per cent over a period of twenty-five years is unquestionably within the capacity of the agricultural industry in the region. In fact, production prospects are such that the embarrassment of further "surpluses" of food is almost assured, unless agriculture in the region becomes more efficiently managed.

CHAPTER

8

Production and Trade in the 1950s

Protection and subsidization of agriculture on a national basis have in recent years been combined with vast technological changes to expand agricultural output to an unprecedented volume. Farmers in nearly every country of the North Atlantic region have been assured of a market for their basic products at reasonably stable, and often high, prices. The response of millions of farmers has been to take advantage of the improved means of production put at their disposal by research, experimentation and large-scale investment. Farms have been mechanized. Large amounts of fertilizer are applied to soils planted with improved seed. Herbicides reduce the competition of weeds, and fungicides and insecticides protect the products. Livestock strains have been improved by careful breeding, aided greatly by artificial insemination and careful culling of herds and flocks. Livestock are fed scientifically and carefully to obtain optimum yields of meat, milk and eggs.

The result has been a prodigious increase in agricultural output nearly everywhere, achieved with fewer men and women on the farms and with no larger acreage in crops — but, as shown in Chapter 4, by a great rise in operating and capital expenses charged against farming, which has limited the improvement in farm incomes.

Between 1952 and 1959 gross agricultural output in the North Atlantic region rose by 13 per cent. In every country except Canada and Sweden output was up over these years, though in several 1959 did not represent the best year in the period.[1]

The great rise in agricultural output in Western Europe since the end of World War II has not been entirely steady. The first postwar year in which there was a good cereals crop was 1948 and progress thereafter was considerable until 1953.

The several years of indifferent weather which followed were partly responsible for the fact that there were only modest increases in output. Beginning in 1956 in some countries and a year later in others, however, large increases in output in most countries were again the rule.

The pattern of output was much the same in the United States over this period: relatively small increases were made from 1952 to 1957, then in 1958 there was a sharp rise, which has since been maintained. In Canada, however, a combination of poor weather and restraints on agricultural output resulted in a very modest rate of increase in the latter years of the 1950s, and output in the early 1960s was actually below the levels of the early years of the preceding decade.

Food production[2] in Western Europe has risen much more

1. Year-to-year fluctuations in agricultural output are large in most countries, due to varying weather conditions. There was an element of "planning" in the reduced output in Canada and Sweden, however, since both countries found themselves in surplus positions, with external markets difficult to locate.

Output data used in this chapter are from OEEC, Paris: *Agriculture,* 1961; and *Agricultural and Food Statistics,* 1959, unless otherwise indicated. The index numbers in the two publications differ considerably, due to changes in method, and are thus not entirely comparable. The new indexes are carried back only to 1952. Also, see FAO, *Monthly Bulletin,* Rome, March 1960, March and September 1961 and April 1962.

2. Of the countries being considered in this study only the United States produces an important amount of nonfood agricultural items — chiefly tobacco and cotton. Elsewhere, agricultural output and food output are nearly synonymous.

Table 8–1. Index of Per Capita Food Output, by Country, 1952/53—1960/61

(1955/56 = 100)

REGION AND COUNTRY	1952/53	1953/54	1954/55	1955/56	1956/57	1957/58	1958/59	1959/60	1960/61
Canada	123	111	81	100	105	87	88	92	94
U.S.	101	98	98	100	100	97	102	101	100
EEC	(92)	(100)	(99)	(100)	(98)	(99)	(105)	(106)	(113)
BLEU	89	90	97	100	92	99	102	96	106
France	89	97	101	100	96	99	98	107	119
Germany	98	103	102	100	102	102	107	102	118
Italy	88	100	92	100	99	96	110	109	102
Netherlands	100	99	99	100	94	100	109	109	118
EFTA	(100)	(103)	(102)	(100)	(105)	(106)	(104)	(107)	(111)
Austria	88	100	93	100	105	109	112	106	118
Denmark	104	106	105	100	104	113	112	107	116
Norway	103	104	103	100	111	105	104	105	108
Portugal	87	106	103	100	99	101	94	95	96
Sweden	116	114	112	100	110	107	103	104	107
Switzerland	105	103	105	100	97	96	105	101	104
U.K.	98	100	101	100	108	106	102	110	115

Sources: Output index derived from FAO, *Monthly Bulletin*, April 1962; population from OEEC, *General Statistics*, Paris, January 1961.

Note: The index on which this table is based excludes all products used for feed or seed, whether domestic or imported, and for production waste. Price weights used are different for Western Europe and North America. See FAO, *Monthly Bulletin*, March 1960.

Figure 8–1.   Index of Average Annual Per Capita Output[a] of Livestock Products, by Area, 1952–1959

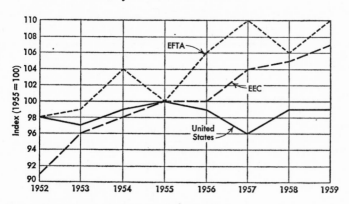

Source: OEEC, *General Statistics,* Paris, March 1961.
a. Excludes livestock produced from imported feed.

rapidly than population in recent years. (See Table 8–1.) The
middle years of the 1950s witnessed, with a few exceptions, considerable stability in food output in relation to population growth.
At the end of the decade, however, very sharp rises in output per
person were recorded. By 1960/61 food output per capita was 13
per cent higher in the EEC countries than it had been five years
earlier and in the EFTA countries it was 11 per cent more. (If
Portugal, where agriculture has remained largely untouched by
modern methods of production, is excluded from the EFTA figures,
the EFTA countries have shown a rise in food output per person
equal to that in the EEC countries.)

Reflecting the changing pattern of demand described in preceding
chapters, output of livestock products in Western Europe rose more
rapidly than general food production. To an extent, this increase
was based on more imported feedstuffs. The percentage of Western
European output of livestock products dependent on feedstuffs from
abroad rose from 8 per cent in 1952 to 12 per cent in 1959.[3] But

3. OEEC, *Agriculture,* Paris, 1961.

livestock products based on indigenous feed supplies also expanded rapidly in Western Europe, by an average of about a seventh between 1952 and 1959 for each member of a growing population. This was in sharp contrast to the United States, where output of livestock products barely kept pace with the rise in population. (See Figure 8–1.)

CROP PRODUCTION

The basis for the sharp increase in output of livestock products in Western Europe in recent years was, of course, greatly expanded production of field crops. The same experience in the United States, unaccompanied by a rise in the per capita consumption of livestock products, resulted in the accumulation of large surpluses of several crops.

Production of every major crop except potatoes (and oats, for which barley is being substituted in many places) reached an all-time high in either 1958 or 1959 for the North Atlantic region, despite the reduction in output in Canada. Potatoes, facing a secular decline in demand nearly everywhere in the region, were produced in no greater quantities in North America than they had been a decade earlier and in Europe production at about 75 million tons was well below previous peak levels.

Otherwise expanded production was the normal pattern for most crops in most countries in the last years of the 1950s. Cereals production (which is discussed in some detail below) reached a total of 285 million tons in 1959, about 5 million tons greater than in the preceding year. Sugar-beet production totaled 65 million tons in 1958. Production of oilseeds, basically uneconomic in most of Western Europe, where production is unimportant and falling, reached an all-time high of 22 million tons in the United States in 1958. Fruit and vegetable production has been nearly stable in most countries of the region over the past decade.

Average annual production of food and feed crops (excluding hay and other grasses) rose between 1948–1951 and 1955–1958 by some 14 per cent in the North Atlantic region as a whole. Only in the United Kingdom was there a fall in crop output, caused largely by a considerable reduction in potato production. In North

America crop production increased by 13 per cent.[4] In Europe the increase was 16 per cent, mainly owing to the very sharp rises in crop production in Italy and France.

Virtually all this increase in crop production came about as a result of increased yields per hectare. This was augmented by a continuing shift in most countries from oats to barley, which has generally resulted in sharp increases in yields.

CEREALS

While improved yields have been the rule for all crops (except, perhaps, fruits and vegetables, for which the information is scanty), and have thus contributed to an ever-increasing degree of self-sufficiency in most countries, it is the record in cereals production which holds the greatest interest for this study. This is true not only because of the predominant position of cereals in relation to other crops, but also because the great bulk of international trade in temperate-zone foods is in cereals and livestock products, in part derived from cereals. Recent history of cereals production demonstrates more clearly than anything else the effort by the Western European nations to supply more of their own needs and the related difficulties in North America to adjust to a changing foreign demand pattern, caused mainly by the European drive toward greater self-sufficiency.

The decade of the 1950s was a period of expanding demand for cereals in Western Europe. This was true despite the fact that the human population of the countries under consideration was consuming per capita a steadily declining amount of cereal products — mainly flour. In many countries population increase was not sufficient to outweigh the declining per capita demand for cereals, with the consequence that total direct demand for cereals was falling. In the nine years from 1950 to 1959 per capita consumption of cereals fell by about 12 per cent in Western Europe, while population increased by 8 per cent.

---

4. The official United States index shows the increase to be about 8 per cent. (USDA, *Agricultural Statistics, 1959,* p. 462.) The difference is accounted for by inclusion of nonfood and hay crops in the USDA index and by the use of different price weights in the index.

However, as direct human demand for cereals fell, demand for livestock products rose sharply. Requirements for cereals for feeding purposes increased more or less commensurately. Consumption of livestock products (measured in terms of animal protein) per person rose in most countries by 2 to 3 per cent per year. As a large part of this fast-rising demand was met from increased output of pork, poultry and eggs in Western Europe itself, the market for cereals remained strong.

Total production of five main cereals (wheat, rye, barley, oats and corn) in the North Atlantic region rose from 216 million tons per year in 1948–1952 to an average of 265 million tons in 1958–1960, well over half a ton per person.[5] About one third of this total was bread grains — wheat and rye. (The division between bread grains and coarse grains is arbitrary, as a considerable amount of wheat is fed to animals, while humans eat substantial quantities of barley, oats and corn or products made from them.) Corn, virtually all of which is produced in the United States, constituted about 40 per cent of total production. Barley and oats made up the remaining quarter, with well over half of it grown in Canada and the United States. Western Europe accounted for only a little over a quarter of all five grains combined. (See Table 8–2.)

YIELDS AND AREA

This increase in production of nearly 50 million tons in less than a decade reflected prodigious feats in agricultural technology.[6] The

5. Total production of cereals, including rice and others not considered here, throughout the world is estimated to be between 250 and 300 kilograms per person per year. If China, the Soviet Union, Western Europe and North America are excluded, the average in 1959 was about 225 to 250 kilograms per person. FAO, *Production Yearbook, 1960,* Rome, 1961.

6. The figure must be seen in perspective to understand its magnitude. The 50 million tons increase is equal to the increase in cereals production in the USSR, where a large expansion in land planted to cereals occurred during this period. The increase alone is equal to two thirds of India's total cereals production and is substantially more than all the cereals production of South America or Africa in most recent years. See FAO, *Production Yearbook, 1960,* Rome, 1961.

Table 8–2. Land Used for, Production and Yields of Five Cereals, by Crop Area, Annual Average, 1948–1952 and 1958–1960

CROP AND AREA	LAND USED (THOUSAND HA.)		PRODUCTION (THOUSAND TONS)		YIELDS PER HA. (HUNDRED KG.)	
	1948–1952	1958–1960	1948–1952	1958–1960	1948–1952	1958–1960
Total, five cereals	128,319	119,408	216,314	264,622	16.9	22.2
Canada	18,681	17,404	24,939	24,022	13.3	13.8
U. S.	81,299	72,207	138,374	169,727	17.0	23.5
EEC	20,276	21,201	36,656	50,636	18.1	23.9
EFTA	8,063	8,596	16,345	20,237	20.3	23.5
Wheat	50,804	43,837	67,529	77,680	13.3	17.7
Canada	10,513	9,060	13,472	11,566	12.8	12.8
U. S.	27,756	21,458	31,066	35,864	11.2	16.7
EEC	10,234	10,868	18,467	24,662	18.0	22.7
EFTA	2,301	2,451	4,524	5,588	19.7	22.8
Rye	4,292	3,624	6,929	7,145	16.1	19.7
Canada	555	213	463	222	8.3	10.4
U. S.	686	655	524	727	7.6	11.1
EEC	2,235	2,047	4,426	5,048	19.8	24.7
EFTA	816	709	1,516	1,148	18.6	16.2
Barley	10,658	15,428	18,231	30,913	17.4	20.0
Canada	2,870	3,399	4,282	4,916	14.9	14.5
U. S.	4,095	5,919	5,843	9,509	14.3	16.1
EEC	1,931	3,321	3,635	8,588	18.8	25.9
EFTA	1,762	2,789	4,471	7,900	25.4	28.3
Oats	26,805	21,479	37,849	35,723	14.1	16.6
Canada	4,623	4,529	6,338	6,554	13.7	14.5
U. S.	15,266	11,793	18,970	17,665	12.4	15.0
EEC	4,281	3,040	7,326	6,578	17.1	21.6
EFTA	2,635	2,117	5,215	4,926	19.8	23.3
Corn	35,760	(35,040)	85,776	(113,161)	24.0	32.3
Canada	120	203	384	764	32.0	37.6
U. S.	33,496	32,382	81,971	105,962	24.5	32.7
EEC	1,595	(1,925)	2,802	(5,760)	17.6	(29.9)
EFTA	549	(530)	619	(675)	11.3	(12.7)

Sources: FAO, *Monthly Bulletin,* various issues, 1960 and 1961.

expanded production was grown on about 7 per cent less land than was used for the same crops in 1948–1952. In Western Europe production rose by 34 per cent, while land in cereals was only 5 per cent greater. Yields were thus up by more than a quarter. In the United States yields rose even more rapidly, by about 38 per cent. Because area was reduced, however, production was up by only 23 per cent.[7] In Canada alone, where weather conditions in the main wheat-growing areas were indifferent, or poor, did yields fail to increase substantially.[8]

As will be seen, most of the increased yields in the region can be laid to changing farming practices. However, it should also be noted that very substantial increases in yields were brought about by switching land from rye and oats to wheat and barley (and, in southern Europe, corn). (See Table 8–2.)

FERTILIZERS AND YIELDS

One of the major factors entering into expanded yields over the past decade was the increased use of fertilizers. Between 1948–1952 and 1958 average annual consumption of commercial fertilizers in the North Atlantic region increased by more than half — from 9.7 million tons to 14.7 million (plant nutrient content). Western Europe used something more than half of each of the chief nutrients — nitrogen, phosphates and potash. Applied on a much smaller area, the amount of fertilizer used in Europe per hectare of arable land was about three times the average in the United States.[9]

7. The figures are not precisely comparable, as the calculation for the United States is based on harvested area, with an allowance for products hogged off or used for silage, while statistical practices differ in the European countries somewhat. However, the margin of error is small.

8. Wheat yields in Canada in the years 1955–1957 averaged nearly 1.5 tons per hectare, about 15 per cent above the averages for 1948–1952 and 1958–1960. FAO, *Production Yearbook, 1960,* Rome, 1961.

9. The comparison is not entirely a fair one, for the United States — and even more so, Canada — has large areas of land in crops in which moisture factors limit the value of applying large amounts of fertilizer. Thus South Dakota farmers used less than two kilograms per hectare of land in crops in 1957. But even in areas more similar to Europe American con-

Table 8–3. Consumption of Fertilizers in 1958, by Type and Approximate Total Consumption per Hectare of Arable Land, by Country, Annual Average, 1948–1952 and 1958

| REGION AND COUNTRY | THOUSANDS OF TONS OF PLANT NUTRIENT, 1958 | | | | KILOGRAMS PER HECTARE OF ARABLE LAND | |
	TOTAL	NITRO-GEN	PHOS-PHATE	POTASH	ANNUAL AVERAGE, 1948–1952	1958
Canada	260[a]	57[a]	126[a]	77[a]	5.2	6.4[a]
U. S.	6,468	2,346	2,230	1,892	(22.5)	34.3
EEC	5,722	1,659	1,968	2,095	76.1	119.4
BLEU	359	101	99	159	263.3	360.8
France	1,949	481	763	705	50.4	91.4
Germany	2,186	575	607	1,004	146.8	251.4
Italy	761	294	386	81	29.2	48.2
Netherlands	467	209	112	146	389.3	445.2
EFTA	2,300	706	809	785	74.7	111.1
Austria	203	43	80	80	45.7	115.0
Denmark	383	105	110	168	95.6	138.6
Norway	135	45	46	44	139.2	161.6
Portugal	148	66	74	8	19.4	35.9
Sweden	266	90	98	79	57.6	72.5
Switzerland	86	14	43	29	124.1	193.2
U. K.	1,079	344	359	376	111.4	152.1

Sources: FAO, Rome: *Production Yearbook, 1958*, 1959; and *An Annual Review of World Production, Consumption and Trade of Fertilizers, 1959*, 1960; OEEC, *Agricultural and Food Statistics*, Paris, 1956.
  a. 1957.

Even in Portugal, where less fertilizer is used per hectare of arable land than in any other Western European country, more plant nutrient is applied than in the United States. In the Netherlands cropping is carried on in a veritable layer of fertilizers — nearly a half ton was used per hectare in 1958 (Table 8–3).

sumption of fertilizers is low. In 1957 it was about ninety kilograms per hectare in Ohio, about eighty in New York. USDA, *Agricultural Statistics, 1959*, Washington, 1960.

Figure 8–2. Crop Production (Wheat Equivalent) and Fertilizer
Consumption per Hectare of Land in Crops (except Hay
and Forage), by Country, Annual Average, 1953–1957

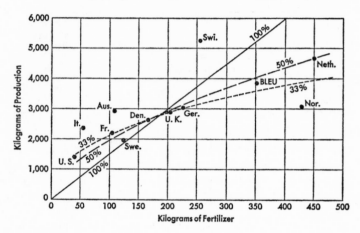

Sources: FAO, *An Annual Review of Production, Consumption and Trade of Fertilizers, 1959,* Rome, 1960; OEEC, *Agricultural and Food Statistics,* Paris, 1959; and Appendix III, Table E.

What sometimes seem to be inflated claims for the value of fertilizers receive some rather impressive support from the yield records in Europe.

The average annual volume of food crop production in the various countries for the period 1953–1957 has been calculated according to an index adapted from the FAO. By dividing the number of hectares in crops into this volume of crop production, a yield of "wheat equivalent" per hectare has been obtained. In Figure 8–2 this yield has been plotted against the amount of fertilizer per hectare of cropped land used in each country.

In general it can be seen that increased use of fertilizer is fairly closely associated with higher crop yields. Thus in the United States, where about 42 kilograms of plant nutrient were applied to each hectare of cropped land, yield per hectare was about 1,380 kilograms of wheat equivalent. In the Netherlands, where over ten times as much fertilizer was used, output was about 4,700 kilograms of wheat equivalent per hectare.

The graph is drawn in such a way that if there were a perfect correlation between fertilizer use and crop production, the countries would all fall along the straight line running diagonally across the diagram. In fact, with a few exceptions, the countries fall below that line, indicating diminishing returns as more fertilizers are applied.

Most of the countries, however, do fall close to the other lines on the graph. These lines indicate that doubling the amount of fertilizer results in a 50 or a 33 per cent increase in production. Belgium-Luxembourg used slightly more than double the amount of fertilizer per hectare used in Denmark, while production was about 47 per cent more. Roughly the same ratios apply to Germany and the Netherlands. The United Kingdom used nearly twice, and Germany a little more than twice, as much fertilizer per hectare as France but had yields only a third higher.

There are, of course, many other factors which go to explain these differences in output per hectare. Apart from differences in climate, there is a considerable range of labor input, in type and quality of soils and in farming methods. Moreover, the exclusion of hay crops and land used for them affects the various countries in quite different ways. Nevertheless, there appears to be sufficient correlation between high fertilizer inputs and high yields to support from national output statistics what agricultural research proved long ago in connection with particular land areas.

The supporting case for increased use of fertilizers, even where yields are now high, is strengthened by a great body of information developed by experiment stations and other institutions. The national statistics confirm the experiments in an impressive way. Figure 8–3 shows the relation between fertilizer consumption and wheat yields in each country. In this chart the horizontal distance between the two ends of each line represents the increase in wheat yield between 1948–1952 and 1958–1960. The vertical distance represents the increase in use of fertilizers per hectare of arable land (including orchards). Thus a slope tending toward the horizontal is a favorable indicator. However, the second favorable indicator is nearness of the line to the lower right corner. Thus Denmark and the United Kingdom are both well placed in relation to other coun-

Figure 8–3. Changes in Average Annual Use of Fertilizer and in Wheat Yields, 1948–1952 to 1958–1960[a]

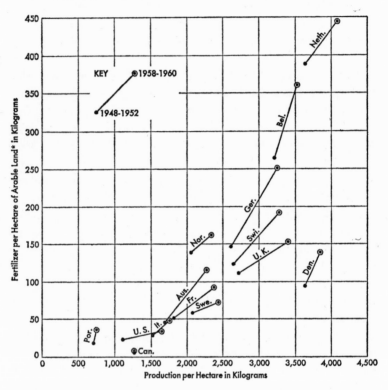

Sources: FAO, Rome: *Production Yearbook, 1960;* and *Monthly Bulletin,* March 1961; and Table 8–3.

a. 1958/59 for use of fertilizer.

* For Canada, sown area only.

tries, but Denmark was getting less benefit from incremental applications of fertilizers than the United Kingdom (to the extent that wheat yields are a proper gauge in this respect).

The slope of the line for Belgium indicates that a point of diminishing returns may be in view. However, the experience in the Netherlands shows that there is no predestined ceiling in regard to fertilizers and yields. The strong horizontal tendency of the U. S. line is somewhat misleading in one respect, as this was a period in which wheat acreages were being rapidly reduced, with the better land staying under cultivation.

ADEQUACY OF PRODUCTION

The extent and the manner of attempting to meet national food requirements from national sources varies rather considerably in the North Atlantic region. Little needs to be said concerning the United States and Canada in this regard. Home supply in the former is adequate or more than adequate to meet all the needs of the country for every nontropical agricultural product except sugar — which, of course, is both a tropical and a temperate product. In Canada much the same situation exists, except for certain fruits and vegetables (as well as sugar).

In Western Europe the situation is more complex. There are six countries which are unquestionable deficit producers of temperate food products: the United Kingdom, Germany, Belgium-Luxembourg, Switzerland and Austria. Three countries can be called "fabricators-in-transit" in the sense that they import large amounts of grain and other feedstuffs and export large amounts of livestock products. These are Denmark, the Netherlands and Norway (whose agricultural industry obtains a major assist from the fisheries industry in the supply of oils and feedstuffs). France and Italy resemble to an extent the North American countries, with most domestic requirements met from home production and with developing surpluses of some commodities available for export. Finally there are Sweden, which apparently intends to adjust its production of nearly all items to domestic requirements only, and Portugal, which is generally self-sufficient at a low level of output and consumption (except that it imports its sugar from its colonies).

All European countries except Norway and, in normal periods, Portugal depend on imports for a large part of their supplies of fats (other than butter). No oil-bearing crop has been developed which can be grown economically in most of Europe. Marine oils, however, meet a part of the need.

PRODUCTION AND IMPORTS

Of a total average annual supply of about 175 million tons (wheat equivalent) of all crops (other than hay and forage) in the years 1953–1957, more than three quarters was produced in Western Europe itself. Human consumption of vegetable products averaged some 109 million tons in those years, with 85 million tons produced domestically. Of the 66 million tons of various crops (wheat equivalent) devoted to livestock feed annually, only a quarter came from imports. (See Table 8–4.) The EEC countries were 87 per cent self-

Table 8–4. Average Annual Crop Supply by Source and Use, and Extent of Self-Sufficiency, EEC and EFTA, 1953–1957[a]

	WESTERN EUROPE	EEC	EFTA
	MILLION TONS, WHEAT EQUIVALENT		
SOURCE			
Total supply	175	118	57
Domestic production	133	99	34
Net imports[b]	42	19	23
USE			
Feed, seed and waste	66	42	24
Domestic production	48	33	15
Net imports[c]	18	9	9
Direct human consumption (or export)	109	76	33
Domestic output	85	66	19
Net imports	24	10	14
	PER CENT		
Extent of self-sufficiency	78	87	58

Sources: Appendix III, Tables D and E; OEEC, Paris: *Agricultural and Food Statistics,* 1959; *Agriculture,* 1961.

a. Excludes hay and forage crops.   b. Includes oil cake and meal for feed.

c. Estimated imports of cereal feeds, bran from milling imported wheat and oil cake and meal imported as such as well as that produced from imported oilseeds. Also includes a small amount of fish meal.

Note: See Appendix III for weights used in converting various crops to wheat equivalent.

Table 8–5. Average Annual Supply of Livestock Products, by Source, and Extent of Self-Sufficiency, EEC and EFTA, 1953–1957

SOURCE	WESTERN EUROPE	EEC	EFTA
	MILLION TONS, WHEAT EQUIVALENT		
Total supply[a]	182	115	67
Domestic output[b]	160	104	56
From domestic feeds	142	95	47
From imported feeds	18	9	9
Imported products, net[c]	10	2	8
	PER CENT		
Extent of self-sufficiency	85	90	75

Sources: Appendix III, Table E; OEEC, Paris: *Agricultural and Food Statistics,* 1959; and *Agriculture,* 1961.
a. Includes milk used for feed.
b. Excludes milk used for feed, which is included in total supply.
c. Meat, eggs, butter, cheese and condensed and evaporated milk.
Note: See Appendix III for weights used in converting livestock production to wheat equivalent.

sufficient in the supply of crops, and the EFTA countries 58 per cent.

Domestic production of livestock products in Western Europe was even more impressive. Of a total supply of some 182 million tons (wheat equivalent, including milk fed to livestock), only 18 million tons originated from imported feedstuffs and 10 million tons (net) were imported in the form of finished products. Self-sufficiency was thus 85 per cent — 90 per cent in the EEC countries and 75 per cent in the EFTA. (See Table 8–5.)

The Importance of the United Kingdom and Germany

The figures given above for the general degree of self-sufficiency in the supply of temperate food products in Western Europe disguise the dominant position of Britain and Germany as the major importers, both from other European countries and from overseas.

Of average annual total net imports of nontropical foods of 52 million tons (wheat equivalent) in 1953–1957, Britain and Germany accounted for 42 million. The other countries imported the wheat equivalent of 10 million tons of foods, almost entirely vegetable oils, on a net basis. They also had net imports of 9 million tons of feedstuffs, but they exported — largely to the United Kingdom and Germany — an equivalent amount of livestock products. (See Table 8–6.)

Apart from the two major importers of nontropical foods, then, Western Europe was supplying nearly all of its requirements from its own resources. In the late years of the 1950s most of the countries were net exporters of at least some of the most important food products. In the period 1956–1959 France could claim net sales of

Table 8–6. Average Annual Net Imports of Nontropical Foods and Extent of Self-Sufficiency, Selected Western European Areas, 1953–1957

		EEC			EFTA		
TYPE OF IMPORT	WESTERN EUROPE	TOTAL	GER-MANY	OTH-ERS	TOTAL	U. K.	OTH-ERS
MILLION TONS, WHEAT EQUIVALENT							
Total net imports	52	21	12	9	31	30	1
Vegetable foods (ex. feedstuffs)	24	10	5	5	14	9	5
Livestock products (finished)	10	2	4	–2	8	15	–7
Livestock products (from imported feedstuffs)	18	9	3	6	9	6	3
PER CENT							
Extent of self-sufficiency							
Production[a]	85	90	83	94	75	58	98
Output[b]	81	88	77	93	68	49	97

Sources: Tables 8–4 and 8–5 and sources shown therein.

a. Total production divided by sum of production and net imports.

b. Output (production less feed, seed and waste) divided by sum of output and net imports.

cereals, pork and cheese. The Netherlands and Denmark were net exporters of every major livestock product. Norway had net sales of eggs, butter and cheese; Sweden of pork, butter and eggs.[10]

VALUE OF TRADE IN FOOD

In 1959 over one third of the $9.5 billion in imports of nontropical foods and feedstuffs by the individual member countries of the EEC and EFTA originated in Western Europe.[11] The United States supplied about 12 per cent of the total, Canada 6 per cent, Australia and New Zealand over 9 per cent and Argentina 6 per cent. Other countries furnished about a third. (See Table 8–7.)

The United Kingdom and Germany imported nearly two thirds of all the traded foods and feedstuffs originating in Western Europe and over 60 per cent of that coming from outside. Each bought foods and feedstuffs worth more than $1 billion from other Western European countries. Germans purchased more than half their import requirements from other European countries, the British over a quarter. Commonwealth preference, as well as tradition, marked the British pattern of purchases from overseas. Australia and New Zealand supplied 20 per cent of total imports, Canada 9 per cent. By contrast, Germany bought only 6 per cent of its requirements in these three Commonwealth countries. Its purchase of 14 per cent of total imports from the United States was roughly equal in value to Britain's 8 per cent — nearly $300 million in each case. None of the Commonwealth countries had a heavy stake in other European markets, but the United States supplied nearly a third of the imports of Denmark and the Netherlands and almost a quarter of those of Belgium-Luxembourg and Norway.

On the west side of the Atlantic the over-all volume of imports was much smaller. Canada obtained more than half its imports of nontropical foods and feeds from the United States. In return it

10. OEEC, *Agriculture,* Paris, 1961.

11. Defined for this purpose as the thirteen member countries of the EEC and EFTA plus Greece, Iceland, Ireland, Spain, Turkey and Yugoslavia. The values are c.i.f. and are based on import data for the calendar year 1959. OEEC, Paris, 1960: *Trade by Commodities;* and *Analytical Abstracts.*

Table 8–7. Value of Nontropical Food Imports[a] and Per Cent of Total Imports from Selected Areas, by Country, 1959

IMPORTING COUNTRY	VALUE[b] (MILLIONS)	PER CENT OF TOTAL, BY AREA OF ORIGIN							
		WESTERN EUROPE				CAN-ADA	U. S.	AUSTRAL-ASIA	ARGEN-TINA
		TOTAL	EEC	EFTA	OTHER				
Canada	$ 513	9	3	5	1		57	8	—
U. S.	1,943	15	6	5	4	13		9	2
EEC	4,624	41	23	12	6	3	14	2	6
BLEU	438	43	33	6	4	5	22	1	7
France	926	24	15	5	4	2	4	1	2
Germany	2,084	52	29	15	8	4	14	2	5
Italy	568	47	17	22	8	2	8	1	14
Netherlands	608	21	13	5	3	3	32	1	10
EFTA	4,904	31	12	11	8	8	10	16	6
Austria	180	44	24	9	11	6	9	1	4
Denmark	243	26	10	8	8	1	31	2	6
Norway	131	32	10	15	7	6	24	1	3
Portugal	51	24	8	6	10	2	3	1	3
Sweden	250	47	17	21	9	1	14	2	5
Switzerland	306	48	39	8	1	6	12	1	3
U. K.	3,743	28	8	11	9	9	8	20	7

Sources: OEEC, Paris, 1960: *Analytical Abstracts;* and *Trade by Commodities.*
a. SITC groups 0 (less 07), 22 and 41; for Switzerland, group 0 only.
b. C.i.f., except Canada and U. S., for which value is f.o.b.

exported to the United States roughly the same dollar amount, but furnished only about an eighth of the total American imports. Neither bought much from the Western European countries. Movement of nontropical foods from east to west across the North Atlantic amounted to only about a fifth of that in the opposite direction. Argentina, the main Latin American exporter of nontropical agricultural products, supplied the EEC and EFTA countries with 6 per cent of their imports. The chief buyers were the United Kingdom, Germany, Italy and the Netherlands (Table 8–7).

The total import bill of $9.5 billion for nontropical foods in the thirteen European countries in 1959 was offset to some extent by food exports valued at $3.7 billion. The net deficit of $5.8 billion was, however, a very large item in the trading accounts of European countries. In only four countries did net exports of foods and feedstuffs serve to offset trade deficits allocable to imports of similar items (and in two of the four, Norway and Portugal, the surplus of exports of foods and feedstuffs was attributable to fish and fish products rather than agricultural commodities).

The European countries taken together have been eminently successful in selling their nonagricultural products in international markets in recent years. In four of the six EEC member countries the value of nonagricultural net exports was more than sufficient to pay for the nontropical foods and feedstuffs they purchased abroad in 1959. Italy's net imports of nonagricultural goods added $49 million to the cost of its net agricultural imports. In the Netherlands, the only net exporter of foods, sales covered about half of the deficit in other trade. For the six countries taken together net sales of nonagricultural commodities were 38 per cent more than the net value of their imports of foods and feedstuffs.

In the member countries of the EFTA, however, the situation was different. Their net import bill in 1959 of $3.3 billion for nontropical foods and feedstuffs was only partially met by Britain's surplus of about $2 billion earned from selling other goods. Denmark alone came close to balancing its net expenditures for nonagricultural goods with its exports of food. The United Kingdom, by far the most important buyer of nontropical foods and feedstuffs, fell about $1.5

billion short of meeting its import costs for these items by export of other goods. (See Table 8–8.)

The total cost to Western Europe for imported nontropical foods and feedstuffs of $9.5 billion was nearly a quarter of the value of its total imports in 1959. In a world economic situation in which the balance of international payments takes on ever-increasing importance for nearly every country, and in a circumstance of growing dissatisfaction of farmers in industrialized countries with their relatively unhappy economic status, no democratic government can afford to turn a blind eye to agricultural problems which might be found solvable within the scope of its own legislative powers.

It is in this context that the arguments for continued, even strengthened, protection and support for agriculture in Europe are found by many to be persuasive. A decline of only 1 per cent in the

Table 8–8. Net Exports of Nontropical Foods and Feedstuffs and Other Goods, by Country, 1959   *(Millions)*

COUNTRY	NONTROPICAL FOODS AND FEEDSTUFFS	OTHER GOODS
Canada	$ 556	$–1,047
U. S.	857[a]	1,539
EEC	–2,452	3,395
BLEU	–286	139
France	–438	965
Germany	–1,890	3,217
Italy	–189	–243
Netherlands	351	–683
EFTA	–3,320	304
Austria	–135	–42
Denmark	575	–795
Norway	58	–563
Portugal	11	–196
Sweden	–162	–41
Switzerland	–216	–14
U. K.	–3,451	1,955

Source: OEEC, *Analytical Abstracts,* Paris, 1960.
a. Includes approximately $800 million of exports under disposal program.
Note: Exports are f.o.b., imports c.i.f., except for Canada and the U. S.

volume of agricultural output in Europe (at agricultural prices prevailing there in the late 1950s), if replaced by imports, would add
between $200 million and $250 million to the import bill, even at
the more favorable prices prevailing on the international market.
It is enough to make even liberally inclined governments pause — a
fact of which farm spokesmen are aware.

> The 60 per cent increase in the output of home agricultural pro-
> duction over this period has enabled this additional demand for food
> to be supplied from home resources without having to import more
> food from overseas. If further increases in population are not to be-
> come a charge on the balance of payments, we must see to it that
> the long-term trend in home agricultural production is allowed to
> move upwards also.
>
> Expansion is the theme on which everyone is agreed. The state of
> the national economy and the state of agriculture are interdependent.
> If agriculture is depressed, the economy will be depressed. The
> buoyancy of our economy therefore depends in no small measure on
> the existence of a healthy agriculture. This is a thought that must
> guide all future Governments.[12]

The "healthy agriculture" in Britain in the year Lord Netherthorpe spoke the words quoted above received from the Treasury
$434 million in deficiency payments to make up the difference be-
tween what the farmers actually received for their output and what
they and the government had agreed was the right amount to keep
agriculture "healthy." That amounted to almost exactly the total of
farm operators' net income. In addition, farmers had received $224
million in fertilizer subsidies, plowing grants and a long list of other
items. They also had some tariff protection and some of their prices
were maintained by applying seasonal import quotas on selected
products.[13] The year 1959 was also one, however, in which a replacement of only 13 per cent of domestic agricultural output by

12. Lord Netherthorpe, President, National Farmers' Union, The George
Johnstone Lecture, 1959, *Agriculture and Its Relation to the National Economy and Industry*, Seale-Hayne Agricultural College, Newton Abbot, England, 1959.

13. *Annual Review and Determination of Guarantees, 1960* (Presented to
Parliament by the Secretary of State for the Home Department, the Secretary
of State for Scotland and the Minister of Agriculture, Fisheries and Food),
HMSO, London, 1960; OEEC, *Fifth Report*, Paris, 1961.

imports would have wiped out Britain's entire surplus on current account in its balance of payments — and only six years earlier agricultural output had been that much lower.

European food imports remain large, despite the impetus to domestic production given by protection and high guaranteed prices. The prospect now is that they will decline during the next decade, despite the fact that good economics and resource allocation argue for a different outcome. No one should expect the *Economist* to write again, as it did a century ago:[14]

> What is the present *home* policy of England, stated in a single sentence and disencumbered of any unnecessary and subordinate details? It is the policy of free trade. It requires that the prosperity of the great seats of industry should be fostered — that the growth of the great pursuits of industry should be developed — whatever may be the consequences and the cost. There is, indeed, no reason to suppose that the agricultural interest has suffered from the legislation of late years. . . .

14. *The Economist,* London, June 15, 1861, as reprinted on June 17, 1961. The legislative reference is to the repeal of the Corn Laws in 1846.

9

Expanding the European Food Supply

Under the circumstances described in earlier chapters there is no reason to doubt that agricultural production in Western Europe will continue to expand. Agricultural policies of national governments in recent years were autarkic. The Common Market proposes to do very little more than combine at least six countries, and probably more, to form a larger protected market.

The certainty with which this view of the future can be expressed derives mainly from the politico-economic roots of Europe's farm problem as much as it derives from the still unutilized technological improvements available to the agricultural industry in most of Western Europe. We will turn again to the effect on production of the interplay of familiar social-economic factors (too many farmers demanding higher prices to compensate them for inadequate land-holdings). Here it is perhaps worth while to review very briefly some of the technical factors which point in the direction of more farm output, in both Europe and North America (as well as in other parts of the world). Numerous full accounts are available from both national and international sources which show how far most farmers are from realizing the full potential gains in output offered them by technological advances.

Farm Consolidation

It was seen in Chapter 3 that European farms, for a number of reasons not equally applicable in all countries, tend to be small. Statistically, of course, the picture is far from clear. It is not always possible to say whether a particular farm is small because it is a part-time occupation for its operator or whether its operator holds another job because his farm is too small to occupy him on a full-time basis. Nor can it be expected that this sort of question can be answered — and stay answered — in an industry undergoing the sort of transformation common to agriculture in most European countries.

Nevertheless, it is clear enough that farm consolidation will tend to lead toward increased output. Much of the technology on which expanded production depends is, for practical purposes, applicable only where its heavy capital costs can be spread over farms large enough to permit economic utilization. This is obviously true of mechanization and highly specialized equipment such as modern dairying requires. There is, however, a somewhat more subtle relation between adequate farm size and output levels. In the main it has to do with owner attitudes toward the use of new techniques, which generally are first adopted on larger farms and only gradually penetrate to smaller farms.

The agricultural policies of most European countries include efforts to consolidate farms into more economic units.[1] In Austria present plans call for consolidation of farms covering an area of 600,000 hectares by about 1970. Belgium, which probably stands in greater need of farm restructuring than any other country in Northern Europe, has a program calling for consolidation which by 1966 will affect some 25,000 hectares annually. In Germany, where farms are generally small and in some areas badly fragmented, the number of farms of less than ten hectares fell between 1949 and 1959 by about 220,000 — about 15 per cent — while farms of over ten hectares increased by about 30,000. Policy calls for continued

1. OEEC, *Agricultural Policies in Europe and North America* (especially the Second and Fifth Reports), Paris, 1957 and 1961.

effort to consolidate farms, about three quarters of which are still less than ten hectares.

The Foundation for Land Administration in the Netherlands operates to acquire land and then to resell it to farmers wishing to expand their holdings. The number of holdings of one to five hectares declined by 40 per cent during the 1950s. Dutch farm policy calls for continuation of the effort to increase the average farm size. Sweden and Norway have continuing programs of land consolidation with a number of compulsory features. In the United Kingdom and Denmark the problem tends to be of relatively less importance, though land utilization and, to some extent, land transfers are subject to considerable supervision and are influenced by financial policies. France and Italy, whose problems tend to be regional with respect to the need for land consolidation, have done much less in this field than most of the other European countries.

Mechanization

Rapid and widespread mechanization of farming operations has taken place in Western Europe in the last decade and there is little reason to believe that it has reached its limits in any country.

The relation between mechanization and expanded farm output is complex and not easily demonstrated statistically in many cases. In some parts of Western Europe additional mechanization is coming about as a response to high labor costs and, in some areas, to a very real shortage of farm labor. To some extent this investment is substitutional. It would not necessarily have a direct effect on output.

However, even labor-substitutional mechanization is changing farming methods in a direction which — under the cost-price relations existing in recent years — tends toward greater output. In cereals production mechanization has been partly responsible for shifting land from rye and oats to wheat, barley and corn — all of which are more efficient crops from the standpoint of optimizing yields per hectare. Mechanization is directly related to the improvements in grass production and the use of silage feeding methods. Substantial improvement in yields has resulted from the much greater ability to take advantage of propitious weather conditions for land preparation, seeding and harvesting now possible with machines.

Mechanization in agriculture has already had an impact on livestock output, but there is unquestionably much more improvement to come in many parts of Western Europe. Bringing feed to the animal, rather than sending the animal out to bring it home itself, is closely linked to extended mechanization. Animal maintenance rations are reduced, permitting achievement of appropriate slaughter weights more rapidly. While mechanization is, of course, not fully responsible for this sort of change in production methods, it is a necessary condition to following such methods on an economic basis.

The growth of mechanization of agriculture in Western Europe has been phenomenal. Figure 9–1 indicates the growth in numbers of three important items of farm equipment in Great Britain and in the European Economic Community (excluding Italy) between 1950 and 1959. Tractor numbers in the EEC multiplied by more than five times, there were a dozen combine harvesters in 1959 for every one in 1950 and there were six times as many milking ma-

Figure 9–1. Approximate Growth in Numbers of Major Items of Farm Machinery in Western Europe during the 1950s

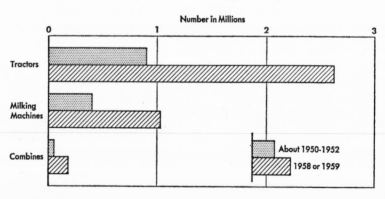

Source: Estimates based on data in FAO, *Production Yearbook, 1960*, Rome, 1961.

chines. In Britain, where agriculture was already much more highly equipped than on the Continent in 1950, the rises were somewhat less spectacular. Nevertheless, Britain is probably the best-equipped country with respect to agricultural mechanization.

It is not necessary for the farmers of Western Europe to continue to expand their stocks of mechanized equipment at these recent rates in order to obtain more output (or lower costs, or both) from them. It takes time to learn to use equipment efficiently. An ECE/FAO study[2] cites underutilization of tractors in Europe in recent years. Sample studies showed 60 per cent of all farms used their tractors less than 400 hours per year. Only 3 per cent used them in excess of 800 hours, which was considered an economically adequate working time. In Britain average annual working time per tractor was estimated at about 600 hours.

It is thus reasonable to anticipate fuller utilization of equipment in Europe. This would not necessarily result in greater farm output, but, combined with the other factors considered here, it would be surprising if it did not.

Improvement of Breeds and Varieties

Despite the fact that Europe has been a pioneer in the development of improved breeds of livestock and higher yielding varieties of crops, application of this knowledge has been far from complete. Even with policy changes which might in other respects damp down trends toward greater output, it is safe to predict that utilization of better breeds and strains will have a steady and important upward pressure on production.

More Fertilizers

Almost inseparable from the impact of new and improved varieties on crop production is the part played by application of more — and better balanced — fertilizers. Reference has been made in Chapter 8 to close correlation of yields and fertilizer consumption.

Although the two factors are closely linked under most circumstances, it is important to note some fundamental differences. A

2. *Towards a Capital Intensive Agriculture*, Geneva, 1961, Part I, p. 30.

worsening of market prices may in many circumstances result in a reduction in the use of fertilizer, or at least a reduction in the rate of increased use. Thus a reduction in the prices farmers in Denmark received for cereals, which occurred in the middle of the 1950s, was accompanied by a nearly negligible increase in the use of fertilizers. With the introduction of price guarantees at somewhat more favorable levels, fertilizer utilization again began to climb.

Worsening prices, on the other hand, may hasten the utilization of improved varieties of seed as a means of improving the return to the producer. This factor probably helps to explain the rapid adoption of hybrid varieties of seed corn in the United States during the 1950s when feed-grain prices were relatively unfavorable.

In Western Europe — or in most parts of it, at any rate — the prospect is for additional utilization of fertilizer to accompany a general improvement in the varieties of crops and grasses seeded.

Better Farm Management

All of these existing trends — larger farms using more mechanical equipment, planting improved varieties of crops supplemented by additional, more properly balanced fertilizers and feeding better-bred livestock by more efficient means — will be maintained in Western Europe, barring a radical change in farm policy. At this juncture they will be joined by another development of a different sort which is only beginning to have a general impact on farm production.

The 1960s will mark the first time in history in which a measurable number of Europeans becoming farm operators for the first time will have had any training for the job other than that provided by tradition and propinquity. There are some notable and important exceptions to this generalization, particularly in Denmark and the Netherlands, where scientific farm management has been fostered by formal educational institutions and informational services conducted by the governments and by cooperatives for many decades. In most of Europe, however, for generations men who operated farms had learned most of what they knew from behind the horse — or the pair of oxen.

Men born in the twenty-five years from 1890 to 1915 probably represent a majority of farm operators in most countries of Western Europe.[3] This is true for a number of reasons. Their fathers and older brothers constituted the main casualties of World War I. Most of the present farm operators came of age with Europe in the economic doldrums — when security in the village seemed preferable to the uncertainties of an unknown industrial world. The younger farm operators in the 1930s might, in time, have left the land voluntarily. Most found themselves pulled off farms and into armies in 1939, and many did not return to farming. Those too old for military service remained on the land and when peace was restored found themselves "too old to move." They have remained in charge of their farms beyond their years because their sons and their younger brothers who survived World War II found urban jobs waiting for them after the first years of postwar adjustment.

This generation of old, inadequately educated farmers was asked, quite suddenly, to apply a great accumulation of scientific knowledge to their farming operations. What had been learned and accepted gradually over a century in America (and in a limited area of northern Europe) was urged upon these men in the years following World War II by greatly expanded educational services, by farm demonstrations, by salesmen of farm equipment and supplies. A great many men, already middle-aged or more, without personal knowledge of an internal combustion engine of any sort or of an electric motor were urged to use complicated machinery powered by these little-understood motors. Men trained almost solely by tradition were asked, rather late in life, to apply the methods of modern business to farming operations which, until recently, had employed only a modicum of analysis and accounting. The wonder is not that so many failed to make the shift; it is rather that so many were able to make at least a partial adaptation to a new way of farming in such a brief period.

These farmers will now disappear at a progressively rapid rate. Many will not be replaced and their land will be consolidated in larger, usually more efficient, farm units. But as they replace the old, the new farm managers will come increasingly from a gen-

3. ECE, *Economic Survey of Europe in 1960,* Geneva, 1961, Chap. 3, p. 42.

eration whose experience with the modern world will be vastly greater than that of their predecessors. Many of them will have had some specialized education in agricultural subjects. Nearly all of them will have had experience in the military services, where they will have been exposed to varying amounts of education in operating mechanical and electrical equipment. Many will have spent their young adulthood on farms which have been, in these recent years of rapid change, more efficiently managed than the average.

It is not possible, of course, to quantify the effect on production of this growing "modernization" of European farmers. It will occur simultaneously with the changes indicated earlier in this chapter. In the three largest producing countries — France, Italy and Germany — the impact could be startling. In all three appreciable percentages of total agricultural land are in the hands of small landholders who presumably constitute the bulk of those farmers unable to adapt themselves to modern methods. In France and Italy mechanization has not reached an optimum point. (This is perhaps true for Germany as well, although tractor density is high.)

The least that can be said is that, under the favorable price conditions which now characterize European agriculture, improved farm management will certainly contribute to a rise in output and, in all probability, a measurable decline in production costs.

POLICIES AND FARM OUTPUT

Much of what has been described as in store for European agriculture will take place almost irrespective of changes in national agricultural policies or the effects of a gradual integration of those policies in an expanded Common Market.

Two studies of major importance with regard to future farm production and the problems of bringing it into harmony with prospective consumption levels have appeared recently.[4] A group of

4. EEC, *Tendances de la production et de la consommation en denrées alimentaires dans la C.E.E., 1956 à 1965,* Brussels, 1960; and ECE/FAO, *European Agriculture in 1965,* Geneva, 1960, mimeo. Certain projections in the latter study were extended to 1970 in ECE, *Economic Survey of Europe in 1960,* Geneva, 1961. The author of this study, in conjunction with P. Lamartine Yates, also made certain production and consumption estimates

experts drawn from member countries of the EEC reviewed in detail the outlook in that area to 1965. The Committee on Agricultural Problems of the ECE, working with FAO, extended this review to the other countries of Europe. The studies are comprehensive, and well worth the detailed review of anyone in the major exporting countries still entertaining hopes for large European markets in the future.

The ECE/FAO document projects that total food output in Western Europe will rise at an annual rate of 2.25 per cent.[5] While the projected rate for EEC and northwest Europe, which comprise the main commercial market for imported foods, is somewhat lower (about 2 per cent per year), it is still a growth rate treble that for population. Even in the event that per capita food consumption rises very rapidly, as assumed in the ECE/FAO study, perceptible inroads on the market for nontropical imported foods in Europe will have been made by 1965.

With an anticipated increase in wheat production of 3 to 4 million tons in the Common Market between 1954–1958 and 1965, net imports there are expected to be virtually nil (though some imports of hard wheat may be expected to offset exports of soft wheat). An increase in production of 4 million tons of feed grains (along with a reduction of a million tons of grain fed to draft animals) is expected to meet all, or more than all, the additional needs for feed. Total cereals output, at about 55 million tons, will be sufficient to reduce imports in this important market by 3 to 5 million tons over the period, leaving net import requirements at some 4.7 to 6.6 million tons. And it should be emphasized that the EEC analysts base their requirements on an expected rather rapid expansion of food consumption during this period (substantially greater than that projected in Chapter 7 of this study). A some-

---

for 1970 for J. Frederic Dewhurst, John O. Coppock, P. Lamartine Yates and Associates, *Europe's Needs and Resources,* Twentieth Century Fund, New York, 1961.

5. Western Europe as defined in the ECE/FAO study includes more than the countries under consideration here: the EEC; the EFTA, as well as Finland and Ireland (grouped with the EFTA countries except Portugal to form "other northwest Europe"); and Greece, Spain, Turkey and Yugoslavia, which (with Portugal) form a group called the "Mediterranean countries."

what more conservative estimate of the growth of consumption could reduce estimated deficiencies in home production of cereals considerably.

In the other countries of northwest Europe the ECE/FAO analysis suggests that domestic production of wheat will meet half the needs in 1965, with import requirements falling slightly. Larger output of coarse grains — an additional 2 million tons — may meet most of the requirements for additional livestock output, but the EFTA area, especially Britain, will remain a considerable importer of meat and, perhaps to a reduced extent, butter from outside Europe.

In all the other main nontropical food products except vegetable oils continental Europe will be largely self-sufficient. The United Kingdom is expected to be the only substantial importer of sugar by 1965 and will, of course, remain a major importer of vegetable fats.

A Longer View

The European production outlook described above runs only to 1965. Fundamentally it is based on improved crop yields, continued switching from oats and rye to barley and corn, better grassland practices, higher yields of livestock products per animal and per unit of feed. Only minor changes in land under cultivation are expected to occur, but higher livestock numbers are forecast.

If the relatively rapid increase in per capita consumption of food, particularly meat, assumed by these studies in fact takes place, Europe by 1965 will remain a large, but moderately declining, market for most nontropical foodstuffs and feedstuffs.

The studies themselves imply, however, that their authors have probably minimized their projected output estimates. The EEC analysts write of the prospect of wheat surpluses and even suggest that the Community may be engaged in giving away wheat as "foreign aid." They see ahead a surplus of 4 to 6 million tons of milk — 400,000 to 600,000 tons of cheese, approximately — against a surplus of only about 10 per cent that amount in the late 1950s. A deficit in sugar of 137,000 tons will be replaced by a surplus of

500,000 tons. All this — and more — is to come from an increase in output of only 2 per cent annually.

> . . . it seems hardly possible to doubt that the cumulative advance in farm technology and the resulting increase in productivity which has been observed during the past decade can be taken as the starting point for an analysis of the likely development of European agriculture during the years to come. . . .
>
> . . . With no widely acceptable alternative to present agricultural policies in sight it seems highly doubtful at this stage that the stimulus of relatively protected prices and markets will disappear. Even if the orientation of policies be moderately changed, the current tendencies towards higher output per unit of resources seem likely to continue. We are still in the middle of a strongly upward technological evolution in agriculture and the momentum of this evolution is such that it seems likely to be carried further even if policies are devised to discourage production from exceeding a certain limit, and such has indeed already been the experience in several countries. . . .
>
> . . . Thus, for Europe as a whole, the existing potentialities for further increases in production can be found in (a) the lack of any sign that the countries or regions with higher levels of productivity have reached a limit, and (b) the fact that there is every reason to assume that countries and regions with lower average levels of productivity will in most cases follow the path of those above them. . . .
>
> Though the rate of increase may slow down in certain sectors or regions where average yields are high the upper limit has hardly anywhere been reached, and past experience moreover indicates that this is generally never as near as it is thought to be. . . .
>
> . . . [it] seems safe to predict that the general upward trend in average yields and total production will continue over at least the next five years. . . .
>
> . . . For none of the products dealt with in this paper have the rates of increase achieved between 1949–53 and 1954–58 in north-western Europe been used. Of course should they be achieved production would move still further ahead of consumption than has been assumed. . .[6]

The words quoted are clearly those of analysts making less than maximum predictions concerning future output. Moreover, they cite in considerable detail the known opportunities for increased

6. ECE/FAO, *European Agriculture in 1965*, Geneva, 1960, pp. 22, 26, 27, mimeo.

production and the trends toward making use of them, and then minimize their almost certain effect on production. The estimates must be considered to be conservative.

If we look beyond 1965, the outlook for expanded production in Europe is even more impressive. None of the calculations made in connection with the studies cited take account, for example, of the prospects for low-cost feedstuffs of high quality based on "artificial" proteins derived from the unique ability of ruminants to convert nitrogen in the form of urea to protein in the course of digestion. Used in connection with many cellulose materials now of little more than waste value, this supply of protein feed could radically change the methods and costs of feeding cattle and sheep.

The projections in the EEC and the ECE/FAO studies place only minor dependence on improved grassland management and on the extended use of silage for feed. Both developments have only recently begun to gain general acceptance in large regions. Both studies largely ignore the importance of continuing improvements in cattle, which, with the progressive replacement of cows by progeny of the carefully selected sires used in artificial insemination programs, tend to be cumulative for a considerable period.

Factors of this sort, together with further improvements in farm management of a more traditional kind, can scarcely lead to any result other than a prolongation of the upward trend in farm output in Europe, unless very fundamental changes in policies are adopted soon. As noted earlier in this study, agricultural planning within the EEC calls for policies which are almost certain to accentuate the adoption of farm methods most conducive to increasing output. Recent experience in Europe and North America (and, above all, in Japan) leaves little doubt that a high price structure, guaranteed markets and access to the prerequisites for modern farming lead producers to expand output, even at mounting costs.

The Economic Commission for Europe, extrapolating the findings of the studies referred to above to 1970, draws the following conclusions: [7]

7. ECE, *Economic Survey of Europe in 1960,* Geneva, 1961, Chap. 3, pp. 32 and 39.

Agricultural output has been growing very rapidly in Western Europe during the last decade, and although it is generally agreed that the margin for further expansion is still wide, opinions vary as to the rates of growth that might be attained. It may be — although agricultural experts do not think it likely — that in the countries with the most advanced agricultural techniques, diminishing returns will offset the gains from technical progress. But if this were true, there would still be ample scope, even in those countries, for raising standards of farming everywhere to the level of the most advanced farmers — and thus for large increases in output. . . .

. . . By and large, it appears that production is likely to grow faster than demand for foodstuffs in western Europe, even if incomes grow quickly. . . .

. . . The prospect for western European agriculture appears to be increasingly one of surpluses of certain key products. . . .

INTEGRATION AND OUTPUT

The studies cited above were made when the main lines of a common agricultural policy in the EEC had been drawn, but they do not in general take into account the effect of market integration on output prospects. This is perhaps reasonable, as it has generally been recognized that unification of the agricultural market in Europe would at best be attained only slowly. Nevertheless, the underlying assumption of this study, that only a long-range program for agricultural adjustment is a realistic approach to a rational solution of the problems, requires that the effects of integration be taken into account.

The price structure is the most important aspect of a common agricultural policy in Europe as it relates to output projections. This is analyzed in some detail in Chapter 11. All that needs to be said at this point is that the political factors are such that prices for farm products in Europe are likely to be high enough to be conducive to greater production.

Apart from prices, however, there are some other aspects of market unification which may well influence the level of farm output. The most obvious is a furtherance of geographical specialization. With trade inhibited as it has been by national agricultural policies, some rather peculiar patterns of production of some commodities have evolved. This is particularly true of many fruits and vegetables and sugar beets, but it extends to most products in some degree. With increasing concentration of agricultural activity in areas having natural advantages of soil, climate and favorable seasons, there is likely to be a certain amount of impetus given to production.

Great changes in methods of food processing and marketing are already underway in Europe and market unification is likely to induce more of them. While the effect of such changes on output is indirect, it would appear from American experience that developments such as contract production tend to increase output of some commodities.

Market integration in Europe is likely to be accompanied by a considerable growth of highway transportation, a factor of importance in the selection of cropping patterns and livestock densities in areas remote from large urban markets. The effect should be improved profitability in such areas and consequential inducement to more output.

Against these factors leading toward expansion of production as a result of market unification is the factor of exposure of marginal producers to greater competition. The impact of such competition on the output of these producers depends, of course, to a great degree on the price structure, but to the extent that there is a perceptible influence, its direction must be negative.

Perhaps the most influential element in the relation between farm output and a common agricultural policy, apart from the price structure to be adopted, is the extent to which public management of agriculture is "depoliticized." Present plans of the Common Market call for a strong concentration of power over agricultural matters in special organs of the Economic Commission. Until such time as the EEC develops legislative institutions of its own, vesting of power in the Commission tends to represent a partial divorcement of policy, or at least rapid change of policy, from the ordinary workings of politics.

What the effect of a continuing vesting of power in the Commission would be on agricultural production is very difficult to determine in advance. It is easily conceivable that it would represent an increase in the prospects of market stability, the effect of which would probably be to increase production. On the contrary, such a development might be viewed as injecting into the policy-making process an institution substantially less responsive to political pressure than national legislatures have proved to be. This would probably tend to increase the area of doubt and unpredictableness, with consequent inhibitory influence on production increases which might involve risks of evoking policy modifications.

Not too much should be made of the experience of the High Authority of the European Coal and Steel Community as foreshadowing what the EEC Commission might do in respect to agricultural matters, for the industries and their problems are not the same. Nevertheless, it is probably worth pointing out that, whenever differences of consequence arose between the High Authority and the various national industries, the latter found governments generally willing to intervene on their behalf.[8] To the extent any parallel can be drawn, it would seem likely that the Commission would find itself unable to take actions in the field of agriculture which would impede further farm production unless that course appeared the most profitable to farm organizations and their national legislative representatives.

THE OUTLOOK

There seems to be little doubt that the agricultural industries of the European countries, under present policies or those likely to be adopted, are capable of expanding supply at a rate considerably in excess of that expected for demand. It would appear that output can easily be increased at a minimum rate of 2 per cent or more annually — almost double the anticipated rate of rise in demand. If this should take place, European net demand for imported nontropical foods and feeds would be halved by some time in the late 1960s and would virtually disappear over the following decade.

For all intents and purposes only Britain would remain as a net importer of consequence by 1970. Norway, Belgium and Switzer-

8. Louis Lister, *Europe's Coal and Steel Community*, Twentieth Century Fund, New York, 1960; and the annual reports of the High Authority.

land would be relatively minor additional markets which, under the Common Market regime, would be supplied almost entirely from continental surpluses. A market on the Continent might remain for high-quality imported wheat, but this would likely be offset by a more rapid reduction in demand for feed grains and eventual appearance of substantial quantities of European cereals on the international market.

CHAPTER

10

Dimensions of the Agricultural Surplus

From the standpoint of the traditional suppliers of non-tropical agricultural commodities to the European market the picture drawn in the preceding chapter of the future production and demand pattern in Europe is a dark one indeed. Supplies from overseas, which were sufficient to provide all the basic foods for about 35 to 40 million Europeans in the mid–1950s, will be required for only a third that number by 1970. Some time in the 1970s the net market for nontropical foods in Western Europe will disappear entirely. Such is the outlook if present policies remain in force.

In the mid–1950s net exports (including the accumulation of surpluses unsold) amounted to about 15 per cent of total food and feedstuff production in the United States and about 25 per cent in Canada.[1] The total of these exportable surpluses was somewhat in

1. These figures are only approximations and represent the difference between total production and total domestic utilization, whether for food or for feed, seed and waste. In terms of output — final consumption off the farm plus net exports (and accumulation of stocks) — the percentage not consumed domestically was about 20 per cent in the United States and 35 per cent in Canada. It amounted to about 60 million tons of wheat equivalent in the United States and about 12 million tons in Canada. See Chapters 6 and 8 and Appendix III for calculations of volume of food consumption and production.

excess of the net imports of the thirteen European countries whose situation has been examined in this study. Roughly 72 million tons, wheat equivalent, were surplus to North America's own requirements in the middle of the 1950s, while the Western European countries imported about 52 million tons.

Thus, even if Canada and the United States had had in the mid–1950s a monopoly position in exporting nontropical foods and feedstuffs to Western Europe, the only great net importing region of such products, they would have needed to find other outlets for more than a quarter of their excess output. They did not, of course, have such a monopoly. Argentina and Australasia supplied important quantities of these commodities to Western Europe.

Nevertheless, the North Atlantic region (integrated hypothetically, for this purpose) in the mid–1950s was not far out of over-all balance with respect to nontropical foods and feedstuffs. The 20 million tons (wheat equivalent) of net surplus (North America's oversupply of 72 million tons less Europe's deficit of 52 million tons) represented less than 4 per cent of total output of the region. If a policy had existed which had as its aim a pooling of the resources and the market of the region, relatively little adaptation would have been required to make the needs and the output jibe. This would have been true even had Australia, New Zealand and Argentina been added to the region. Their surplus output roughly matched the 20 million tons of North American oversupply but would have still left the total in the neighborhood of 6 to 7 per cent of total output.[2]

Looking forward — and still hypothetically considering the North Atlantic area as a single region for agricultural purposes — it can be seen that the surplus situation is likely to be aggravated rapidly and extensively. By 1970 it appears likely, from the analysis in preceding chapters, that Europe's deficit will shrink by about 30 to 35 million tons, wheat equivalent, in comparison to the mid–1950s. Population increases alone in North America will account

---

2. Calculated roughly from various issues of FAO, Rome: *Production Yearbook;* and *Trade Yearbook;* and preceding reports in the same series, *Yearbook of Food and Agricultural Statistics.*

for most of the increased demand there — at most about 5 million tons of output (wheat equivalent) annually. If, as may well develop, the main burden of a falling demand in Europe is borne by North American exporters, any increase in output exceeding about 3 million tons (wheat equivalent) annually — only about 1 per cent of current North American output of food and feedstuffs — would add to the existing embarrassment of mounting surpluses of nontropical foods, unsalable and difficult to give away.

Holding North American agriculture to an increase in output of no more than 1 per cent annually over the next decade or two would require restraints of unprecedented effectiveness. Output in the United States increased at double that rate during the 1950s, despite considerable effort during most of the period to hold it back. Nearly every factor working toward increased yields and output mentioned in the preceding chapter as being applicable to Western Europe is also pertinent to the American situation.

The amount of political and economic mischief arising from this unprepossessing outlook for trade in agriculture in the North Atlantic region could be very considerable. Little political astuteness is required to predict that hopes and plans for expanded international trade in industrial products could be seriously jeopardized by a shrinking international market for foodstuffs based on autarkic agricultural policies in Europe. Many problems of a political nature were raised by the joint efforts of Canada and the United States to limit competition in commercial grain markets over the past decade. They will be compounded as the European market is progressively taken over by France and Italy and supplies of soft wheat from these countries intensify competition in a shrinking world commercial market. Even European entry into the "give-away market" would create many additional opportunities for friction.

ARE SURPLUSES INEVITABLE?

This, then, is the dismal outlook for commercial agriculture in the industrialized countries of the non-Communist world — countries which have grown closer together economically in recent years. Western Europe, the only important international market, will become progressively self-sufficient in nontropical foods by expanding its production by no more than an unspectacular annual growth rate of 2 per cent. Unless North America (and Australasia) wish to add further burdens to themselves in the way of producing unsalable surpluses, they must limit their increases in output for some time to about 1 per cent per year.

Under existing agricultural policies more surpluses are inevitable. If policies are to be changed enough to make the problem of agricultural surpluses manageable, they should be changed in concert by the North Atlantic countries (and Australasia). Agriculture should not be treated as a thing apart from the main stream of international economic integration. The rightness of the underlying logic, political and economic, of the idea of further integration of the West applies to agriculture as much as to industry. If it is right to reshape the economic structure of the North Atlantic region to make it more mutually interdependent in the supply of many primary materials and manufactures, it is surely proper to extend that interdependence to the production of food. In fact, unification of the market makes more sense for agriculture than for many other sectors of the economy, for there are greater potentialities in agriculture for economical geographical specialization.

The difficulties facing governments, if they make an effort to integrate the agricultural market, are awesome. Governments will be met with every sort of argument to preserve the special position of agriculture in individual countries. There will be great temptation to take the easy way out — to let the farmers go on producing whether or not there is an effective market for their output. Most of the industrial countries of the North Atlantic region are rich enough, and their farm populations small enough, to make it economically and politically possible to go on subsidizing agriculture by one means or another. The most popular means, so long as it can be employed, is to "let the farmer get his income in the market place" — the market place being specially sealed off from the rest of the economic world by exclusionist devices and made specially safe by governments willing, when necessary, to become the residual purchaser of anything offered for sale.

FOOD SURPLUSES, HUNGER
AND DEVELOPMENT

Subsidization of farmers, however it is accomplished, breeds surplus production in the circumstances now faced by the industrialized countries. Are the surpluses really such bad things? After all, there is hunger in the world and there are developing nations which need external help. Cannot our embarrassing riches in food feed the hungry and provide the basis for strengthening the economies of the new nations — and some of the older ones, as well, which have failed to take their places in a modern economic world?

The short answer to that question, contrary to all the public utterances in support of the idea, is simply "no." It is true that donations — "concessional sales" is the current euphemism to describe this process — of food can help to improve the diets of a few million people who unquestionably are hungry most of the time. No person well disposed toward his fellow man would contend that surplus food, once produced, should be withheld from people who need it.

Two facts, however, tend to make the easy, humanitarian approach doubtful, if it becomes a basis for agricultural policies in the industrialized countries which are easily capable of producing surplus food. First, experience of the United States in recent years definitely suggests that there is a physical limit to the amount of food which can be given away in poor countries to which we wish to send it. Port facilities, storage capacity and handling systems have appeared as limiting factors in country after country. To expand and improve them to facilitate greater shipments of gift food which might, for a number of reasons over which the recipient countries have no control, be ended or sharply curtailed would be economic folly, unless a good prospect existed that such gifts could be replaced after a period by commercial imports. Unhappily, few underdeveloped countries which can use our gifts of food now can look forward to a time when they will be able to buy large quantities of food from abroad.

Physical factors, therefore, set a low ceiling on the demand of poor countries for food from abroad, even if it is supplied at little or no cost. However, there is a much more compelling reason to oppose a policy which would attempt to expand these transfers of food from the rich to the poor, however humane the motives. What we are doing even now may be contributing to more hunger in the future.

It is difficult to name an underdeveloped country which does not have as its most pressing requirement improvement of its own agricultural system. Almost nowhere in the underdeveloped parts of the world does agriculture provide a satisfactory foundation for industrialization, although it is quite generally accepted by those who have analyzed national economic growth that growing efficiency in agriculture is a virtual necessity to economic development in all but the most unusual circumstances.

Giving away food to poor countries is perhaps a humane act, but only in the short run. It diverts away from agriculture the investment efforts which might otherwise be taken by governments. The imports compete with domestic food production and are thus an impediment to greater profitability of domestic agriculture and hence a drag on private investment and development in agriculture. Much of the donated imports never leaves the port cities, in many countries the most important markets for food entering into commerce. The existence of the imports slows the development of transportation facilities between the rural areas and the main markets and constitutes thereby a hindrance to the necessary conversion of more farmers from a subsistence to a commercial basis. All these things slow the development and modernization of an underdeveloped country's most basic industry, agriculture, from which more than half the population normally gains its living.

The Economic Commission for Europe, viewing the prospect of undisposable farm surpluses in Europe, used gentle but unmistakable language to describe the weakness of food grants as developmental aid — weaknesses affecting both donor and recipient:[3]

3. ECE, *Economic Survey of Europe in 1960,* Geneva, 1961, Chap. 3.

. . . These advantages are short run: the longer-term disadvantages of such a policy cannot be disregarded. In the donor countries such disposals do not promote the necessary structural adjustment of agriculture, and thus both prolong the need for agricultural support and perpetuate surpluses. In the recipient, under-developed, countries, disposals may save some foreign exchange in years when bad harvests necessitate imports, and, at any time will alleviate hunger or help to build up a food reserve. To that extent disposals are beneficial. . . . Although some industrializing countries undoubtedly attach high priority to food imports, it is unlikely that many of them would regularly import food in preference to other goods if given a free choice in the use of foreign aid funds. Moreover, if surpluses are given only spasmodically, or in years of particularly heavy surpluses in the donor countries, they may even have a harmful effect, on balance, on the rest of the world. In short, a scheme of agricultural surplus disposal does little in the long run to further the economic growth which would eventually make the developing countries independent of foreign aid. In an important sense, the value, as economic development aid, of a disposal scheme is secondary and cannot outweigh its real shortcomings as an effective long-run policy either at home or abroad.

There can be no question in the minds of reasonable men that the industrialized countries of the West have a clear duty to assist in the development of every poor area on earth which has developable resources. It is much more than a matter of political expediency or "competition in the cold war"; in a very fundamental moral sense the nations which have preempted a large part of the world's natural resources available for industrial purposes over the past two centuries, which have effectively closed their borders to large numbers of persons who would have migrated toward their prosperous economies, owe a basic debt to the rest of the world. That debt can be discharged in only one way — by helping to hasten the modernization of the laggard countries. And certainly it is the duty of the West to proffer its assistance to a hungry underdeveloped world in a manner which will promote, not stultify, the most important existing industry — agriculture — in nearly every one of the underdeveloped areas.

It is not surplus foods grown in the West under economically dubious farm policies that the industrialized countries — if they are truly interested in the hungry people of the world — must send, but rather some "surplus" science and development in agriculture: "surplus" knowledge of effective plant and animal breeding, "surplus" techniques of pest control and food preservation. And to back up transfers of knowledge we need to send "surplus" steel and oil to build and operate nitrogen fertilizer plants, to operate "surplus" tractors and earth-moving equipment and to pump water through "surplus" pipe; "surplus" trucks, fueled with "surplus" oil, should move over farm-to-market roads built with "surplus" cement. For surely, in our underworked economies, these things are as truly surplus as our foodstuffs.

These are the means for real economic development. Many people in the underdeveloped countries know this and this is what they want from our developmental aid programs — in agriculture and in industry. They ask for stones — economic foundation stones — and we offer them bread.[4]

Before closing off this argument concerning the limited place that food surpluses donated to underdeveloped countries can have in their modernization, the rather pungent remarks of one economist may be of interest with respect to American surplus disposal programs in general.[5]

4. There is a somewhat sophisticated argument which is generally used in support of the common practice of making part of our assistance loans and grants in the form of agricultural surpluses. It is best stated in an FAO document, *Use of Agricultural Surpluses to Finance Economic Development in Underdeveloped Countries — A Pilot Study in India,* Rome, 1955, the work primarily of an eminent American economist, Mordecai Ezekiel; the idea is quantified in a later FAO publication, *Development Through Food; A Strategy for Surplus Utilization,* Rome, 1961. This argument has to do with counteracting the inflationary tendencies which normally accompany developmental investment. Sometimes it is described as making possible the domestic budgetary support needed to mount a development program — selling donated food to the people in lieu of increasing taxes to provide the funds for investment. The argument is mathematically sound, of course. What it largely disregards is the disproportionate burden thrown on a single sector — agriculture — in the financing of the development program. This comes about mainly through the depressing influence of the imported foods on domestic farm prices — actual reductions in some cases, but more commonly price increases less than proportionate to the rise in prices in other sectors of the economy.

5. Jacob Viner, "Economic Foreign Policy on the New Frontier," *Foreign Affairs,* July 1961, p. 567.

Our farm policy is integrally related, in terms both of conflict and of harmony, with all phases of our economic foreign policy as a whole. For strategic reasons it commonly masquerades in internationalist costume, but if we penetrate its superficial disguise, it will be found to be essentially and narrowly domestic, isolationist and even internationally aggressive.

In the farm program of the Kennedy Administration, the internationalist disguise is made more elaborate. We are urged to embark on a Food for Peace Campaign, and we are asked to stop talking of agricultural "surplus," but to speak of "abundance," an abundance to be shared with the poor and the hungry, at home and abroad. Our agricultural superiority over the Soviet Union is to be transformed into a diplomatic weapon "to shape the future of the world." The "surplus," or as I prefer to call it, the "excess," is to be transformed, as far as *production* is concerned — as distinguished from *stocks* — from an incidental, unintended and transitional by-product of schemes to raise farmers' incomes to a permanent feature of our economy. The irresistible demands for subsidies of the farmers and of their Congressional spokesmen are to be tied up in one tightly-wrapped package with the humanitarian objective of relieving hunger abroad, the strategic objective of outmatching Soviet aid to poor countries, the foreign policy objective of aiding underdeveloped countries to attain higher rates of economic growth, and, to bring it quite up to date, the need for correcting our balance-of-payments deficit. The taxpayer, who bears the cost of the subsidies to agriculture, is assuaged by being assured that it is cheaper to give our abundance away than to store it.

11

Principles of a Common Farm Policy

There apparently will be more surpluses in agricultural output in the North Atlantic region and there will be little useful to be done with them. This is the only reasonable conclusion that can be reached from a review of plans, policies and trends in the individual countries in the region and of the embryonic common agricultural policy of the Common Market.

In a world in which purely national considerations would dictate the response to this outlook, the course of future events would be fairly easily foreseen. In fact, it would be very similar to the course which until now has been followed. Protection of agriculture would be maintained and — as more countries approached virtually complete self-sufficiency — the myriad rules, regulations and techniques governing the importation of the supplies previously needed from abroad would be dropped in favor of simpler prohibitions. Variable levies on imports, to be used by the EEC according to present policies, would replace tariffs, quotas, "mixing regulations,"[1]

1. A device by which millers of wheat are required to purchase local output in specified amounts before they are authorized to obtain imported wheat. The technique has been widely used in Europe.

state trading and the many other inhibitory techniques by which foreign supplies have been quantitatively controlled.

This may turn out to be the pattern of the future. It is clearly the present plan of the European Economic Community. It would simply mean that the traditional exporting nations, with their existing surplus output problems exacerbated by a decline in European imports, would make the entire adjustment in production when the domestic political circumstances in those countries would no longer tolerate farm production for which no market — not even an absorptive "giveaway" market — existed.

There are some reasons for believing that this outlook is a little too pessimistic. First, there is the very real prospect of declining protectionism in the industrial sectors of the economic structures of the industrialized countries. The extent of tariff cutting which might well take place over the next few years with respect to manufactured products and some raw materials and basic metals could go far to unify the market for those goods. A trend which has been in existence for a few years on a very selective basis might quite soon be strengthened by much more general reductions in tariffs.

It is difficult to believe that agriculture can continue to be fully exempted from this trend, despite the disappointingly autarkic character of the present EEC common agricultural policy and our own national policies. Unquestionably the traditional agricultural exporters among the industrialized countries will make great efforts to reduce the rigidities of the common agricultural policy as it now exists. The United Kingdom has a substantial interest in preserving as much as possible its current position, by which it meets a considerable part of its import requirements at very low prices compared to those which will prevail in the EEC.

A second reason for thinking that some degree of liberality may survive the current trend toward nearly complete autarky in agricultural policy making lies in the realm of real comparative costs and the more than negligible burden that extreme protectionist policies for agriculture place on the rest of the economy in a number of countries. Economic policies which tend to reduce protection accorded industrial products must take account of the injurious effects on their production costs which result from perpetuating within the economy a high-cost sector of any considerable size. Failure of each major economic sector to "pull its own weight" can be tolerated when protection is accorded to most producers of goods of any sort. When that protection is reduced for an important part of an individual economy, as may now occur for most manufactured products, the remaining protected sectors — if they are of the size of agriculture — will be seen more clearly to be impediments to keeping competitive the costs and prices of those goods newly exposed to full international competition.

These factors hold out hope for a less rigid system of protection for agriculture and less complete scope for its application than recent trends have suggested. It would be wrong to place too much dependence on their strength. Whatever economic rightness there may be in pressing agriculture into the somewhat more competitive world market which seems to be in the making for most goods, it remains a fact that farmers retain a singularly powerful influence over policies affecting them. They have successfully made themselves wards of government to a degree unmatched in most countries by any other important group of producers. They have been exposed to a minimum of the rigors of competition in any meaningful sense of that term. There should be no expectation that "free competition" in the production and pricing of farm products is in prospect, in national or in international markets.

What must be done is to obtain the agreement of governments — for they will be the guardians of the welfare of farmers for a long time to come — that "economizing" in the field of agriculture is important, even if the ordinary machinery of competition which economizing generally depends on is not operable in dealing with farm problems. The power of the market place has been effectively dethroned as the arbiter for determining the economic effectiveness of farmers. For periods which vary in different countries farmers have operated in a situation in which they have not been required to "answer up" to any economic audit, for governments failed in the main to substitute their own systems of evaluation when they ruled out price competition for a wide range of farm products.

RESPONSIBILITY OF GOVERNMENTS

Governments, if they are responsible, do not meet their obligations to their constituents merely by lifting particular industries out of the jostle of the market place, no matter how necessary that action may be. No matter how a society is organized, a fundamental objective must be "optimum allocation of resources" — "getting the most for the least" — "economizing." In classical theory — and in practice to a much greater extent than its critics admit — the play of the market performs this function by providing for a free and fluid situation in which payments to "the factors of production" can be made and be changed in response to an ever-changing situation with respect to demand and costs.

That theory of a free market — of a sort of economic Darwinism endlessly rewarding the strong, eliminating the weak, absorbing mutations — conforms to the facts of economic development in a general way. But it has been vastly interfered with, and economic institutional history of the past two centuries of developing industrialization is largely a recitation of society's efforts to make the theory work in practice in some cases and to prevent its working in others.

When the action has been to prevent its working — as it has in agriculture in most countries in recent years — there has been an implicit responsibility placed on governments to act in a manner which ultimately would bring about the same result as would have obtained under a working free-market situation. The objective has remained the same; only the means of getting from here to there has been modified. The socialist technocrat has achieved perfection when his economy is operating, in terms of resource allocation, exactly as that described — though not predicted — by Alfred Marshall. Every man would be in his right place, using just the right amount of materials and capital to produce just the right set of products to satisfy the totality of human wants. Moreover, every man would be ready and able to move frictionlessly to a new right job, using the new right amount of materials and capital to adjust to a technological change or to a new right set of products demanded to satisfy a new totality of human wants.

That is perfection, in a socialist or in a free economic society or in one in which there are large elements of both competitive freedom and centralized direction — the latter describing almost all modern economies. It has never been closely approximated. Seldom, however, have governments abandoned it as a guideline to the extent they have in dealing with agriculture in the last two or three decades. Regulative bodies deal with many industries in which the competitive method of resource allocation is unworkable, with the primary objective of obtaining a final result which simulates that which would have come from competition had it been workable.

Such a criterion is notable by its absence in the substitution by governments of public decision taking for private in the field of agriculture. Academic journals abound with criticisms of agricultural policies in terms of improper resource allocation. Rarely is this criterion used when agricultural policies are discussed in parliaments or in agricultural ministries. It is not that legislators and bureaucrats are not accustomed to analysis based on the criterion of efficiency. Much is said with respect to the problem in other economic sectors — about too much or too little investment in transportation or steel or the automobile industry, about labor "featherbedding" on the railroads or in the pilots' cabin of airliners, about the reduction of competition when large firms drive small firms to the wall by fabulous advertising expenditures or by local and selective price cutting. All of these matters have periodic airings in governments, and they are fundamentally based on the question of proper resource allocation.

The public debate on agriculture, until now at least, has not centered on the efficiency of farmers in the sense of economizing in the utilization of the totality of resources employed to meet a particular market situation. Instead, it has concentrated on how that market situation can be rigged to see that farmers get their "fair share" of national income. In this process the basic economic argument has largely been lost to sight. The treatment which farmers receive from governments is more "social" than "economic" — more like the benevolence accorded to the aged or the blind or the war veteran than the impartial economic justice which governments must try to hand out in maintaining a climate in which efficient economic decisions can be taken.

The revolution in farming techniques is indeed throwing up in its wake social problems of major proportions. They must be met. But the overriding requirement is that the economic criterion of efficiency — of proper resource allocation — be restored to its place of primacy in making agricultural policies. The very process of modifying farm policies toward this end — of making public management of agriculture simulate in the results it obtains the kind of resource utilization which would prevail if this were a more competitive world — will itself intensify the social problems. But a hard truth must be faced: farm policies have consisted of an inharmonious mixture of welfare and economic objectives and the result has been that they have largely failed to achieve either satisfactorily in most industrialized countries.

THE REQUIRED BASES FOR A UNIFIED MARKET

What would we have to do if we set out to make North Atlantic agriculture conform to our plans for market integration for other industries?

First, it would be necessary to obtain international agreement that a situation of excess production in fact exists. The belief that what is wrong is merely an indequate system of marketing tends to linger for a long time in the minds of those, on and off the farm, who deal with agricultural surpluses. Only recently has it come to be widely appreciated in the United States, hoisted uncomfortably astride its growing mountain of cereals surpluses, that the problem is really one of overproduction — that, in the circumstances prevailing in its home market and abroad in recent years, no amount of tinkering with the marketing process could move an appreciably greater volume of wheat and corn. It is doubtful that European producers and governments have in fact generally reached this conclusion.

Second, there must be general understanding in the entire North Atlantic region that the mere existence of a net deficit supply position in any one country does not signify that that country is not a "surplus producer." Wheat grown in Germany at a cost of $100 a ton is indeed more "surplus" than wheat in storage at Fort William on the Great Lakes, delivered there by farmers at half that price and deliverable to a German port at two thirds the cost of German wheat. This may appear to be a self-evident statement. That it is not generally understood is a fair measure of the extent to which compartmentalization of the market has confused the basic economic concepts and issues.

Third, unification of the North Atlantic agricultural market would require acceptance on the part of governments that all countries have a part in the process of adjustment of supply to demand. As mentioned above, continued autarky, even on an area basis as planned by the Common Market agricultural policy, shifts the burden of adjustment entirely on to the traditional exporting countries. The other side of this coin is that a policy of gradual unification of the market cannot, in any immediate period, shift all of the burden of adjustment on to the highest cost producers. We are not dealing here with the creation of a "freely competitive market" for agricultural products. Rather, what is being discussed are the problems and the principles and techniques involved in government management of agriculture which will, after a time, result in a market situation which roughly simulates the circumstance which would have prevailed had agriculture been subjected to about as much international competition as other industries.

If the idea of a reasonably unified agricultural market in the North Atlantic region were to be accepted as an objective of the governments concerned, the political and economic implications of the three points made above would have to be found acceptable. That would mean production controls in all countries, surplus and deficit alike. It would mean that a reasonably unified price structure (which might allow for moderate tariffs but not other trade restraints) would be established as an objective to be reached in stages. Finally, it would mean that the heaviest burden of adjustment would ultimately fall on the least efficient producing countries, though in the interim the more efficient countries might be required to modify their output policies most.

What would this mean in practice? For all intents and purposes it would mean that an agreement should be reached as to the probable distribution geographically of cereals production in, say, 1970 or 1975, if the concept of relative cost advantage is to be taken into account. Once agreement is reached as to how the production side of a unified market would look under the cost-respecting hypothesis, the individual countries would undertake to guide their cereals production policies toward it in a progressive manner, with respect to both prices and output.

Before describing this process quantitatively and indicating some of the politico-economic difficulties attendant on it, it is desirable to explain why the problem relates mainly to cereals. While wheat and feed grains have been very large elements of trade volume in nontropical commodities in the past, there have been considerable quantities of other products moving toward Europe — meat, butter, seed oils and oilseeds and certain fruits.

With respect to oilseeds, they are not in fact "temperate" products in the European sense of the term. No variety of oilseed crop has been developed so far which can be produced competitively in northern Europe. Rapeseed (colza) is the only one of any consequence sown and its importance is minor. Soybeans and peanuts, particularly the former, can and probably will be produced increasingly in southern Europe. However, production is at present of virtually no importance in relation to oil requirements.

Fruits imported into Europe are largely tropical or citrus, the latter falling on the borderline between tropical and temperate. If Greece and the Iberian countries are in some way integrated into a European market, citrus production in those countries can be greatly expanded on a competitive basis. They, with southern Italy, are already producing a substantial amount of the northern European imports of oranges and lemons (grapefruit, from the standpoint of both production and consumption, is only beginning to find a place in the European market). Moreover, the countries bordering the southern and eastern shores of the Mediterranean are already large and growing producers of citrus fruits for the European market on a fully competitive basis.

Butter trade is large, but it is unique in that the United Kingdom is the only country obtaining appreciable quantities from outside Europe, a demand which is met to a very large extent by New Zealand and Australia. Expansion of milk production in Europe at increasingly competitive costs is safely predictable, particularly if cereals acreages are limited and grass output is expanded. The progressive disappearance of the British market for butter produced outside Europe can be expected, even under conditions of only little or no protection for European milk producers.

Much the same reasoning applies to the future trade prospects for beef and mutton. Expanded production of grasses will form the basis for larger European output of these meats.[2] Supplemented with feed concentrates in the form of reasonably priced cereals and oil cake and meal, there is no reason to believe that the feed base of Europe's agriculture is inadequate to produce competitively much larger amounts of beef and mutton.

The problem of relative efficiency and geographical specialization, then, comes down mainly to the production of cereals for direct human consumption and for use in feeding livestock, in particular hogs and poultry.

AN UNFREE BUT ECONOMIC
CEREALS MARKET

A rational cereals production and marketing situation in the North Atlantic region by 1970 or 1975 would call for more production in efficient growing areas and somewhat less production in less efficient areas. How much should in fact be grown, and where, can be only a considered guess. It is an unhappy fact that most govern-

2. The potential may be greatly increased by the development of "artificial" feeds for ruminants, by means of combining proteins in the form of urea with low-cost cellulose digestible by cattle and sheep. This method of feeding avoids the expensive process of converting nitrogen into vegetable proteins by growing cereals and high-protein grasses. It permits the soil to be used to produce cheap, high-yielding plants with low protein content, a wide range of which are of such chemical composition that their carbohydrate content can be utilized by the animal. In effect, one stage of "manufacture" performed by agriculture — the conversion of nitrogen to protein — is eliminated so far as the use of the soil is concerned, and the function is transferred to the digestive system of the animal.

ments, despite the almost limitless statistical analysis they have made of their agricultural sectors, cannot answer one basic question: what are the range and distribution of costs in producing cereals? How much of the crop in a normal year is produced at 80 to 90 cents a bushel, 90 cents to a dollar a bushel, and so on?

Even if this information were known, however, it would not provide very much help in establishing a target situation for production on an economic base ten or fifteen years in the future. Costs are changing and they are changing unevenly. New varieties of wheat which can be made to yield as much as 150 bushels per acre — ten tons per hectare — in the northwest part of the United States probably cannot be used so effectively everywhere, but may be adaptable to some areas. Improved knowledge with respect to the use of more and different combinations of fertilizers can lead to great increases in yields in some soil and climatic conditions, relatively small increases in others. Programs of farm consolidation can be expected to increase output greatly in some European countries, less in others and in North America. Grain farming is still undergoing a period of rapid technological changes — some already adopted in some areas, others not yet widely used in any area. Undoubtedly there are more changes in store, even in a period as short as ten or fifteen years, which are not yet identifiable.

This means that the selection of a production pattern for the future must be tentative and that the policies undertaken to reach it — or a modified version of it — must be flexible. Above all it means that governments must make a continuing effort to find out what the range of production costs actually are and how much and where they are changing. For all intents and purposes, an international effort to rationalize the cereals market is one of simulating the situation a competitive system would have produced over a period, but doing it without the benefit of the knowledge which comes from the play of the market.

It would be wrong, however, to think that perfection must be achieved in this comparative production-cost analysis. In view of the political factors which must be taken into account, perfect knowledge of the costs of producing cereals would be — from the standpoint of operating the international market — of little more than academic interest. If governments are willing and able to undertake the job of bringing some rationality into the cereals market over a period of time (as, indeed, they have agreed to do in the Common Market, albeit at a relatively high price level), enough can be learned to guide the controlling mechanism with respect to output and prices. It is much more a matter of will than of knowledge.

The Production Objective

The level of cereals production to be sought in the North Atlantic region ten or fifteen years hence should be that which meets the needs of the region itself.[3]

The actual volume of production needed by then is, of course,

3. This objective can be disputed, chiefly on the grounds it is too high. Those who believe it is too high might rest their case on the belief that Australia and Argentina will not be "phased out" of the business of supplying cereals to Europe by 1970 or 1975. They may well prove to be right. However, it should be recalled that both face the prospect of improving markets closer to home — an outlook which would be even better if the United States and, to a less extent, Canada, ceased to provide cereals in Asia and Latin America under surplus disposal programs at concessional prices.

Another argument for saying that the objective of regional balance in the North Atlantic region is too high concerns the possibility of outlets for the production of developing countries. Dr. Arthur F. Burns, as a member of the Board of Trustees of the Twentieth Century Fund, was critical of this aspect of the present study when it was proposed for the Fund's consideration. Unquestionably the objection is valid if in fact the underdeveloped countries (apart from Argentina) have any cereals for sale at reasonably competitive prices. There can be little question that the argument is quite valid with respect to sugar, the production of which could be greatly expanded at competitive prices if Europe and the United States could be persuaded to reduce output of domestic producers. It is probably also true of oilseeds, insofar as the United States is concerned.

Whether these countries now in process of development will, in fact, have appreciable quantities of cereals for sale on competitive terms a few years hence is, however, more doubtful in this writer's opinion. There is certainly great opportunity for expansion of production in Latin America and Asia. If, in fact, the developing countries are able to supply cereals — or any other item — competitively, a North Atlantic policy should certainly be modified to make it possible to provide a market. Dr. Burns and others (including this writer) believe that a strong and stable market for primary commodities, including cereals, is probably the best form of support industrialized countries can offer to the developing nations at this stage. Protective policies which limit the size and stability of that market are not only unjustified but somewhat nullify other efforts to assist economic development.

subject to some doubt. Very roughly the requirements would rise by about 1.5 per cent per year, due in the main to population increase in North America and to a combination of population increase and a shift from direct consumption of cereals to consumption of more livestock products in Western Europe. This would mean demand for about 250 million tons by 1970 — somewhat less than total production in the years to 1959 and considerably less than the amount produced in 1959–1961. There is thus a need for a certain reduction in cereals output — fairly sharp to begin with, and then more gradual — if production and requirements in the region are to be brought into adjustment. During the period of production adjustment, concessional sales by the United States would be tapered off in a manner calculated not to disrupt seriously the supply situation in those countries now depending on such underpriced imports. At the same time the relatively limited commercial exports of cereals by Canada and the United States outside the region would presumably be declining.[4] Australian sales in Asia would be rising, as would those of Argentina in Latin America.

Price Objectives

There is a widely held opinion that price changes do not play a normal role in affecting agricultural output. Under this theory the farmer has an "asymmetrical" response to changing prices: when they go up he increases his output, but when they go down he also increases his output in an effort to recoup through more production what he has lost in narrowed profit margins. There are unquestionably circumstances in which this rather unbelievable response does take place.[5] To the extent these circumstances in fact prevail,

4. A considerable part of those sales were to Japan until the recent, and presumably temporary, sales of wheat and barley by Canada to China.

5. The circumstances are rather easy to describe in terms of ordinary marginal-cost theory. For one reason or another, the producer is not, when a price reduction occurs, maximizing his profits, i.e., he has not extended his output to the point at which his marginal cost of production is approximately equal to his return (at the former price). He has an unabsorbed profit potential to the extent that his marginal cost is below the price. Therefore, unless the new price comes down far enough to reach his marginal-cost point, he may be induced by the very fact of a reduction in price, and hence in-

they require combined action in the form of both price reductions and production controls to bring about, at least initially, a reduction — perhaps even a stabilization — of output.

The price objective for cereals in the North Atlantic region should be a price level which would require a minimum of direct production controls to keep supply and requirements in balance. No one can say in advance what that price level should be, though it clearly needs to be below that prevailing recently — wheat about $75 to $110 per ton and coarse grains about $70 to $90 per ton in Western Europe, and wheat about $60 to $75 per ton and coarse grains about $45 to $50 per ton in North America.

In terms of relative price levels for all agricultural commodities in recent years it might be guessed that an average entry price of about $75 (including a tariff duty of $7) per ton for American soft wheat (and higher prices for hard wheat) delivered to European ports would accomplish much of what would be required to restrain cereals production in Europe and perhaps North America. This would be roughly comparable to a price of $68 to $70 per ton

---

come, to increase his production and thus regain part of the income he has lost. In other words, he may quite suddenly come closer to approximating "economic man" under the pressure of a loss of income.

It is not necessary to class this (said to be quite normal) farmer as an economic and intellectual dolt for having failed to maximize his profits in the earlier period. He may well have been feeling his way rather cautiously toward a higher level of output in changing technological circumstances with which he was not entirely familiar. He may have felt a lack of trust in the firmness of the market price, dependent, in many cases, on the willingness of his government to go on supporting prices at the past existing level. Under the new pressure of lower prices (still supported by the government) he could perhaps be expected to be a bit more daring in using new methods to obtain greater output, and he could well believe that after one price reduction which has taken place the government will be unable, politically, to lower prices further — indeed, might be tempted to restore at least part of the reduction under pressure from farm groups and legislators.

In brief, the argument in support of asymmetrical responses to price changes is not entirely without support. How important it actually is, quantitatively, is difficult to determine. The statistical case for it in the United States is not very impressive. In Denmark, where farm prices were permitted to drop rather drastically after about 1954, production stabilized to a considerable extent, and, with government action to support prices taken in 1958, output rose sharply. However, there is in fact no conclusive evidence on the point.

to a European wheat grower and about $50 per ton (for comparable grades) to an American or Canadian grower. Coarse grains on the farm in Europe in these circumstances would be worth about $60, which would mean that imported feed grains would have to arrive at European ports at about $56 per ton (including a duty of $5), making them worth about $35 to $37 per ton on a North American farm.[6]

On the face of it bringing about price reductions of these magnitudes would appear to be a large order. The European prices indicated above would be about 25 per cent less for wheat and about 20 per cent less for feed grains than those likely to be selected as the prices to be reached gradually under the EEC's common agricultural policy. In the United States the price of $50 per ton for soft wheat might mean an average of about $55 to $60 per ton ($1.50 to $1.63 per bushel) for all wheat, 20 to 25 per cent below support prices recently in force. Corn at $36 per ton is the equivalent of about $0.90 per bushel, about 15 per cent below what the producer received in 1961. (See Table 11–1.)

These are substantial reductions and probably represent the maximum declines which governments could realistically be expected to achieve, assuming they adopted and faithfully attempted to carry out a policy of rationalizing the market for cereals in the North Atlantic region by about 1970. Two questions must be answered to test the realism and efficacy of such reductions. How much would they cost in terms of farm income? Would they prove effective in bringing about balance in cereals output and the relocation of production in the most economic areas?

6. The calculation of these relative prices is complicated and the figures given here are only approximations. They are based on an average farm-to-market cost and quality differential in Europe of about $7 per ton for wheat and $4 per ton for port-to-farm cost for feed grains. They assume a price differential of about $8 to $10 per ton between wheat and coarse grains on the farm in Europe. The North American prices are based on the European port prices calculated in the above manner, with the cost from American farm to European port averaging $16 to $18 per ton for wheat and $14 to $16 per ton for feed grains. There are, of course, quality differentials, particularly for hard wheat, which, if taken into account, would modify the price estimates shown here. These estimates are based on soft wheat, with American soft wheat carrying an average quality premium over European soft wheat of $3 to $4 per ton.

Table 11–1.   Hypothetical Prices of Soft Wheat and Feed Grains,[a] 1970, and Approximate Reduction, 1960–1970, by Country

| COUNTRY | HYPOTHETICAL PRICES PER TON, 1970 | | PROSPECTIVE PERCENTAGE REDUCTION, 1960–1970[b] | |
	SOFT WHEAT	FEED GRAINS[a]	SOFT WHEAT	FEED GRAINS[a]
Canada	$50	$35	–5[c]	–10
U. S.	50	35	–23[c]	–15
Belgium			–25	–25
France			–15	–10
Germany			–35	–35
Italy			–35	–15
Netherlands			–20	–15
	68	60		
Austria			–30	[d]
Denmark			–10	—
Norway			–35	[d]
Sweden			–20	–25
Switzerland			–45	[d]
U. K.			–5	–20

Sources: 1960 — from FAO, *Monthly Bulletin*, Rome, various issues; International Wheat Council, *International Wheat Statistics, 1961*, London; EEC Statistical Office, *Prix Agricole*, Brussels, 1961. 1970 — see text.

a. Selected feed grains, usually barley; corn for the United States.

b. Based on 1960 prices which are not entirely comparable, but approximate payments to producers.

c. Estimated reduction in price for all grades of wheat. Prices of all cereals rose sharply in Canada in late 1961 as the result of poor crops and extraordinary sales to China, which reduced carry-over stocks.

d. 1960 prices not available.

The Cost of Lower Cereals Prices

The final marketings of cereals (i.e., those which are not used for feed, seed and farm waste) constitute varying proportions of total farm output in the different countries of the North Atlantic region, but nowhere are they dominant. In Western Europe cereals marketed represent a higher proportion of total farm output in Italy than elsewhere, with cereals marketed constituting about 20 per

Table 11–2. Estimated Effect of Lower Cereals Prices on Net Farm Incomes, Selected Countries, 1958–1970

COUNTRY	FINAL OUTPUT OF CEREALS, 1958		PROSPECTIVE PERCENTAGE REDUCTION, 1960–1970	
	AS PER CENT OF TOTAL OUTPUT[a]	VALUE (MILLIONS)	CEREALS PRICES	NET FARM INCOMES
Canada	(25.0)	$ (650)	6	(1.5)
U. S.	(8.0)	(2,500)	20	(3.5)
EEC				
Belgium	8.6	90	25	4.5
France	9.0	675	13	2.0
Germany	10.5	555	35	7.0
Italy	20.2	1,015	33	9.0
Netherlands	4.6	55	18	1.5
EFTA				
Denmark	3.5	40	5	1.5
Norway	6.0	20	(30)	3.5
Sweden	8.5	70	20	3.5
U. K.	9.9	410	12	4.5

Sources: Cereals output — ECE/FAO, *Output Expenses and Income,* Geneva, 1961; USDA, *Agricultural Statistics, 1960,* Washington, 1961; and Canada, estimated. Total output — Appendix II, Table C, with adjustments for U. S. and Canada to eliminate interfarm transactions. Incomes — Table 5–1. Price reductions — Table 11–1.

a. 1956–1959 average for European countries.

cent of the value of all farm output in recent years.[7] The percentages range on down to about 10 in Germany and the United Kingdom, 9 in France and Belgium and well under 5 in Denmark and the Netherlands. In the United States cereals represent about 8 per cent of the value of final farm output, but in Canada they comprise about a quarter of the total. (See Table 11–2.)

These figures demonstrate that sales of cereals to the final market are in fact not very important to over-all farm incomes in most countries in the North Atlantic area. A reduction of 33 per cent in

7. The percentage is probably about the same in Portugal.

grain prices in Italy, which would be most affected, would lower gross farm income by some $300 to $350 million — roughly 6 per cent of gross income and about 9 per cent of net income. A decline of 35 per cent in German prices would cost about 3 to 4 per cent in gross farm income and about 7 per cent in net income. As Table 11–2 indicates, the required reduction in cereals prices in the other countries would affect incomes much less. In none would the impact on net income of farmers exceed 5 per cent.[8]

Measured in this way, the effect of lower prices of cereals on farm incomes in general would appear to be tolerable, assuming output not to be affected very much. The reductions would, of course, strike much more heavily at "cash grain" farmers than at farmers in general. They would absorb not only the losses indicated by multiplying the second column of Table 11–2 by the percentages in column 3. They would also be making a "transfer of income" to livestock producers operating on the basis of purchased feedstuffs (assuming livestock prices would not be directly affected by lower grain prices). This would be of importance in the United States and Canada, but much less so in Europe. Nevertheless, these losses generally are not catastrophic. In an industry in which technology, size of land holdings and number of people employed are changing as rapidly as in agriculture, income changes no larger than those indicated above — if they are spread over a few years — can be taken in stride. Farmers — grain farmers — would not like them, of course. Few, however, would be forced to do more than modify somewhat the pattern of their farming operations. There is far too much dynamism in the agricultural industry in these countries to permit a change of cereals prices relative to other prices to have more than a transitory impact on the level of incomes farmers are likely to enjoy over the next few years.

The Effect on Output

No one can say with any certainty what impact such price reductions for cereals would have on output. Presumably the reduc-

8. These estimates assume that net income (before allowance for interest on employed capital) from grain production is equal, as a percentage of the value of sales, to net income from farming generally.

tions would come about gradually (see Chapter 12), and cost reductions per unit of output might fully offset the lower prices for many producers. However, if the reductions were seen to be inevitable, even though gradual, they might cause anticipatory changes in the decisions of many growers with respect to cropping patterns, expenditures on fertilizers, capital expenditures — all of which might have considerable effect on the volume of output beyond that attributable directly to relatively small annual reductions in prices.

It might be safe to guess that the prospect of a price reduction of 10 per cent or less by 1970 would have little or no deterring influence on production prospects, i.e., cereals farmers as a whole would continue to do those things which contribute to an increase in yields averaging 1 or 2 per cent annually. If the prospective decline in prices ranged from 10 per cent to perhaps 20 to 25 per cent, the over-all response might be one of stabilization of output — some marginal producers would quit producing cereals entirely, others would reduce production by planting smaller acreages, others would cut back by reducing expenditures on fertilizers and other production aids. Such reductions might well be offset by more intensive efforts to obtain higher yields by some producers and others would be willing to take lower unit profits because they had been able to extend their ownership of land. If the prospective reductions in price exceeded 20 to 25 per cent, it is probable that some deterrent effect on output might begin to be felt.

A glance at Table 11–1 shows that if these estimates are within the range of reality, the prospective price reductions for cereals would probably have no deterring impact in Canada. In the United States the effect might be to reduce wheat production somewhat and perhaps stabilize output of feed grains. In most European countries — France, the United Kingdom and Denmark are the main exceptions — the price reductions should have an over-all deterring effect.[9]

9. The reduction shown for France is somewhat misleading, as cereals crops after 1962 are almost certain to carry a substantially higher price guarantee than the 1960 and 1961 price levels used in this calculation.

TRANSITION

As European governments discuss with each other and ponder over the problems of agriculture in a more unified and generally outward looking economy, there is at least a chance (though not yet evident) that they may conclude that achievement of a lower price structure for cereals is not only desirable but politically possible. They may conclude that the economic advantages of maintaining at least some international specialization and trade outweigh the pain involved in facing up to their declining farm populations.

How would they get from here to there? What would be the process of moving from the present high cereals prices to (in most cases) considerably lower ones? How would output in the high-cost countries be restrained during the period of price lowering? How would international trade be managed so that the trade pattern, at the end of the transition period, would be an adequate reflection of relative cost differences in the exporting countries?

The Common Market countries are faced with some of these problems already. In the process of lowering cereals prices in Germany and Italy in the direction of French prices, it has been proposed that price changes be gradual and trade within the area be guided toward free movement by progressive removal of various kinds of restraints. The ideas have not been completely spelled out, and unquestionably the transition will require a considerable amount of improvisation.

Finding answers to these questions in the entire North Atlantic region would unquestionably be more complicated, mainly because the region taken as a whole has a surplus of cereals, while the Common Market still has a net deficit. Nevertheless, some of the plans for the common agricultural policy can be adapted to a broader system.

Quotas

It is difficult to see how the objectives of the transition period can be reached without the employment of minimum import quotas. They would constitute a pressure on the governments of deficit nations to take measures (discussed below) other than price reductions to limit output in the transitional period. Without such actions, particularly in those countries in which prices are far above the ultimate target level, the approach to the equilibrium position would be needlessly complicated. Rising output would probably not be tapered off smoothly, with the probable effect of making timely achievement of the agreed price structure politically difficult, if not impossible.

The import quotas would assume progressively less importance as prices approached the agreed level and would be eliminated altogether when the European countries had reached the stage at which they could depend for protection on only a modest tariff. Initially, however, the quotas would need to be set fairly close to recent import levels and stringently enforced.

The quotas should be established for as large units as possible, i.e., the needs of the Common Market should be combined if possible and the EEC as a whole made responsible for purchasing the agreed amount. This immediately raises the question of the conditions under which cereals would be traded within the Common Market during the transition period. To put the problem somewhat more pointedly, what advantage should accrue to France and other member countries of the EEC with cereals for sale? The answer to this question is easy in principle: French production policy should be geared to reaching the target situation by the end of the transition period, at which time it would have to compete with outside suppliers of cereals with only a minor tariff as protection.

In practice, the advantages accruing to France and the other member countries during the transition period would depend on the methods and prices adopted in connection with administration of the import quotas.

Import Prices

In all probability part of the price which European countries would demand for making the effort to rationalize the cereals market in the North Atlantic region would be the immediate institution of low prices for cereals purchased under the quota arrangement. This would be of paramount importance to the United Kingdom and only slightly less so to several other countries depending on a large volume of imports. To pay the prices which are likely to prevail within the EEC during the transition period would put a heavy strain on their international payments positions.

In these circumstances the non-European supplying countries might properly guarantee delivery of the quantities called for under the quotas at the target prices (which themselves might be subject to some change, of course) throughout the transition period. The period might be begun with a tariff rate considerably higher than that envisaged for the equilibrium situation. Thus a tariff of roughly 30 per cent would have equalized French prices and those of overseas supplies of about the same quality in 1961. This rate might then be reduced toward the target rate by regular steps, thus providing a steady pressure for production adjustment in France and the other exporting countries in Europe.

In itself this system would not provide any particular advantage to France in selling within the EEC. Even though the internal prices in the United Kingdom (assuming it to be a member of the Community) had been raised progressively toward the prices in other countries of the EEC, the British would be unwilling to pay the higher prices for French wheat if they could pay less in foreign exchange to other suppliers. In other words, making room for French exports within the EEC would continue to depend on intra-member agreements (similar to the agreement between France and Germany in recent years) which establish special prices for such transactions.

This would be difficult for France to accept. It sees within the EEC a situation in which it is advantaged in the sale of its high-cost surpluses to other members without subsidization. Yet it is inherent in the proposal for a rationalized cereals market that France make some of the sacrifices. Moreover, there is a strong possibility that France could in fact hold a considerable part of the market at the end of the transition at the level of protection agreed on. A bit of ingenuity displayed during the interim by the members of the Community could probably assist France to make this shift without undue costs of subsidization falling on France alone.[10]

10. For example, other members of the EEC might be willing to pay somewhat higher prices for French wheat and barley if the French government were willing to devote the difference to specified purposes, e.g., additional subscriptions to the European Development Fund.

Exporter Responsibilities

Immediate application of the target prices for sales under quotas would involve continuation of the rather substantial subsidies on American and Australian sales of wheat and the institution of subsidies on coarse grains.

If rationalization of the cereals market is to be reached, the exporting countries must bring to an end their own subsidization of exports. This does not mean that they must end general subsidization of agriculture, but it does mean that the form of such subsidization must be changed to detach it from cereals prices as such. These countries — and particularly the United States — must use the transition period to bring about long overdue overhauls of their own systems of agricultural supports so that no country in Europe — and in particular France — can sustain a claim of "dumping."

Internal Prices

The European nations would enter a transition period with internal cereals prices which are quite disparate. In the interests of general rationalization of European agriculture as envisaged by the over-all objectives of the common policy of the EEC, it would probably be useful for the trading prices of cereals to be brought to the interim protection level — the assured import price plus, perhaps, a duty of 30 per cent as suggested above. This would still leave a considerable gap between present prices paid to producers in a number of countries and the trading prices.

Use of the present British system of deficiency payments would appear to be the easiest means of making any additional payments to cereals growers which would be found necessary in the early years of the transition period. Thus soft wheat would be traded within Europe at prices geared to imports priced at about $88 per ton ($68 c.i.f. plus 30 per cent duty) at the start of the transition. Those countries with higher guaranteed prices would permit trade to be carried on on this basis and would make up by a direct payment any difference between what their wheat growers received in the market and the guaranteed price.

If the trading price within Europe is to reach the target level, the duty must be progressively lowered — by, say, 2 per cent annually.

This would imply that those countries entering the transition stage with guaranteed prices above the trading price would have to make annual reductions in their guarantees amounting to more than the reduction in duties. Thus Germany, for example, would have to reduce its guaranteed price for wheat by about 3.5 per cent annually for the target price to be reached over a period of ten years. Throughout the period the trading price would be lower than the guaranteed price (though toward the end of the period the margin would be narrow), and the German government would be making deficiency payments to its growers over the entire period. Alternatively, it would probably be possible in some countries to bring the trading and guaranteed prices into line much more quickly.

This, then, would be the marketing arrangements for the period of rationalization of the North Atlantic cereals market. Europe, taken as a unit to the fullest extent possible, would undertake to import specified quantities of cereals from outside to be furnished at the prices foreseen for the equilibrium position to be reached in perhaps a decade. Those quotas would be established with the need for internal European trade in cereals kept in mind, this trade to be conducted at prices to be established by agreement between the countries concerned. The overseas suppliers would undertake to end export subsidies for cereals by the time the equilibrium position had presumably been reached, and the European countries thenceforward would depend for protection on a modest tariff only. During the interim period trading prices in Europe would be geared to the assured import prices, plus a duty which would be progressively reduced until the basic tariff rate had been reached. Any additional payments to growers above what they received from the market would be made as deficiency payments, with each government setting its own price levels but all committed to no direct subsidies at the end of the transition period.

THE IMPORTANCE OF STRUCTURAL REFORM

All this effort to bring the production and trading of cereals in the industrialized countries back into the fold of "economics" will be useless — indeed, will be impossible to attempt — unless the nations of the North Atlantic countries employ the next few years in a basic restructuring of their agricultural economies. The proposed point of departure suggested here is limited to cereals because everything cannot be done at once and because the chaotically differentiated cereals market lies at the base of many other disparate aspects of national agricultural situations.

The heart of an agricultural industry reorganized on modern lines, as has been said so often in this volume and by so many other writers, is a reduction in the number of farmers. There are myriad ways in which governments can speed the exodus from farming and ease the distress that such an exodus might produce in individual cases. This is a period of full employment — of actual labor shortage — in most European countries, a time when urban enterprises can absorb all the excess labor which governments can guide from farm to town. In the United States and Canada the problem is somewhat complicated by persistent unemployment even in periods of expanding business activity. That does not excuse governments for failing to take the measures necessary to bring about a modern structure in agriculture matching the technological potential now available. And to a very large extent it must be admitted that this is a government responsibility. Government policies have not been — could not have been — to "let nature take its course" in achieving a new equilibrium in agriculture throughout the industrialized world. There are good reasons why governments should have acted to soften the blows of a technological revolution on farm populations. There are, however, no very convincing reasons why governments, having taken the necessary emergency actions, should not now move on to more basic corrective actions on behalf of agriculture.

Average farm incomes must be improved. They cannot be much improved by more production, because the additional market does not exist nor is it in early prospect. They can be improved in some countries by denying the rest of the population access to cheap food produced economically elsewhere. In other countries high prices which might improve incomes appear sustainable only by making intolerably obvious the misuse of economic resources. It is becoming inescapably clear that the only practicable way to raise average farm incomes is to reduce the number of farmers. In present circumstances in the industrialized countries this is tantamount to permitting efficient farmers to do the production job, each with more land and more capital. Gently, of course, but inevitably, one or more farmers must be "put out to pasture" for each one remaining, just as their horses made way for that one tractor now occupying what on many farms is still called the stable.

How long will it take? Much depends on policies, but it probably can be done more quickly than most politicians tend to think. A quick look at what the next few years may hold in store will end this study.

CHAPTER

12

A Model for 1970

Put very bluntly, the estimates in the preceding chapter
call for governments in the North Atlantic region to act as economically with respect to cereals production and pricing as they
apparently plan to act with respect to most industrial goods. And,
because the disparity in the cost of cereals is at the root of some
other serious agricultural price disparities, a rationalized cereals
market would make possible a rationalized market for a number of
agricultural products.

This proposal is the antithesis of the common agricultural policy
adopted by the original members of the European Community. As
discussed in Chapter 1, that policy effectively insulates agriculture
in the member countries from all external competition. It openly
aims at self-sufficiency. The political content of the common agricultural policy considerably outweighs the economic content,
viewed from the standpoint of "economizing" in the use of resources.

As said earlier, the chief reason that agricultural policy decisions
have such a heavy political bias is the large number of people attempting to make a living from farming. In terms of modern farm
technology the present high man-land ratios in all countries — even
the United States and Canada — are anachronisms. The politics of
agricultural policies has, in effect, taken people — labor — as a

fixed factor in the economic equation, treated prices as a controllable variable and left output as an independent variable (apart from sporadic and feeble efforts at acreage and marketing control). In the circumstances which have prevailed in recent years, a price high enough to satisfy farmers with average, or somewhat less than average, endowments in the way of land and skill has also been high enough to induce farmers with better than average endowments to employ techniques which have as their predominant characteristic large increases in yields. Thus the effort to establish something very much resembling a cartel has failed because the first law of operating a cartel — control of production by efficient as well as less efficient producers — has been disregarded.

With the cartel so mismanaged, the state of agriculture borders on the chaotic — openly so in the United States and France, increasingly so in Canada, less obviously so in the countries with remaining deficiencies in the volume of food production. If the cartel is to be restored to working order (and it must be, for a free market in agriculture, even within one country, ranks at the bottom of political possibilities), a good deal of attention must be paid to workable production controls.

But mere production controls, even if they can be made to work without sinking farming in a deeper morass of administrative regulation than it now finds itself in, almost certainly will not be sufficient. Unless the anachronistic aspects of the agricultural sector are recognized and made the subject of reform, production controls in effect will perpetuate — perhaps accentuate — the inefficiencies of agriculture. The situation requires simultaneous action on all three fronts — the oversupply of labor trying to earn its living from farming, the consequent overpricing of commodities and — consequent to both these things — the mounting need for effective production controls.

REDUCING THE NUMBER OF FARMERS

The number of people engaged in agriculture, as farm operators and as hired workers, has been falling steadily and — in several countries — rapidly. Except in Austria the decline during the 1950s exceeded 1 per cent annually in all countries of the North Atlantic region for which estimates are available. In Germany and Sweden the fall was more pronounced, about 4 per cent per year. In most of the other countries it ranged from 1.5 to 3.0 per cent. (See Chapter 3.)

If the decade of the 1960s witnesses a further decline in the number of people engaged in agriculture at or above the rates prevailing in the 1950s, the root problem facing governments — rigging the agricultural market so that farmers obtain adequate average incomes — will be considerably eased. An annual decline of 4 per cent, which most governments perhaps should adopt as a target, would reduce the number of people in agriculture by a third over a decade. Assuming no change in the amount of land farmed, that would mean that each person remaining would have an average of 50 per cent more land available.

THE MEANING OF A BETTER
MAN-LAND RATIO

No one can say with certainty what the effects would be of an increase by half of the average size of farms. The experience in Sweden is indicative, but not conclusive. While the total amount of labor input fell by a third over the 1950s, the number of hired workers declined even more rapidly. The number of farm units fell by more than 2 per cent annually, but those disappearing tended to be very small holdings. Total agricultural land remained unchanged, but the amount of arable land fell by about 3 per cent. The volume of farm output sagged a little in the middle years of the decade, but recovered almost completely by the end of the period. A decline in the output of crops was more than offset by a rise in livestock products. Gross product (in constant prices) originating in agriculture declined moderately, because the volume of purchased supplies increased. However, gross product per man-year rose more rapidly in agriculture than for the economy as a whole.[1]

In Germany, which also registered a fall in labor input of about

1. The data used in this section are from Chapters 3 and 4 and Appendices II and III and sources shown there.

a third during the 1950s, a considerably different pattern emerged. The number of farms declined by less than 1 per cent annually and the fall was concentrated in farms of between two and ten hectares rather than the dwarf units. Output rose by about 30 per cent, gross product by about two thirds that amount. (In comparing the German and Swedish experiences, it must be understood that German agriculture is much more overmanned than Swedish in relation to land in farms.)

In the United States the amount of labor input fell by about a quarter, virtually all of the decline being accounted for by a reduction in the number of farm operators and family workers. Labor input from hired labor fell little. At the same time farm output rose by about a fifth. Gross product per man-year in volume terms rose much more than the national average (but worsening prices resulted in a much less favorable rise in incomes).

The experience of these countries indicates that, whether farms are large or small on the average or whether the declining labor input is brought about through fewer hired workers or fewer operators, there is no tendency for a decline in output to accompany sharp reductions in farm labor — indeed, output may rise about as fast as it does in countries in which much slower departures from farming are taking place.

This is not entirely a reflection of underemployment of labor on the land in the narrow sense of that term. Probably the most important element in it is the consolidation of land into larger farms under better management. This process of change is unquestionably far from complete in all countries. Even in the United States, where farm consolidation has progressed very rapidly in recent years, only about 40 per cent of the farms in 1959 showed sales of farm products valued at more than $5,000, which is probably less than the minimum gross income needed to employ truly modern production techniques. Perhaps a more reasonable minimum would be $10,000 of cash sales. Only a little more than one fifth of the total number of farms reached that level, though there were 36 per cent more farms selling $10,000 or more in products in 1959 than in 1954.[2]

2. Bureau of the Census, *Census of Agriculture, 1959: Preliminary,* Series AC–59–1, Washington, January 1961.

In most countries of Western Europe the opportunities provided for better farming practices through farm consolidation are unquestionably numerous. Even in the United Kingdom, which has a higher proportion of land in farms of an economic size than elsewhere in Europe, the need for farm consolidation is great. With about the same land area and the same amount of agricultural land as Illinois and Indiana combined, the United Kingdom has about 50 per cent more individual land holdings and uses about that much more labor.[3]

With the possible exception of Denmark, where the very intensive use of labor in relation to land area is apparently quite efficient in terms of output per man, a reduction of labor input in the North Atlantic region of 4 per cent annually would seem to be consonant with stable or rising output. This assumes (as seems reasonable) that the reduction would be accompanied by a rise in purchased materials and equipment, the progressive disappearance of marginal farm operators and their family workers and the consolidation of farms under management which, on the average, would be more able to apply modern production techniques. It is reasonable to estimate that an annual rise in food output of about 1.5 per cent will be sufficient to meet the incremental needs of the region for food. A sharp reduction in the labor force apparently would not imperil that sort of rise in output.

It is in the area of improved farm incomes for a smaller number of farmers that the rapid reduction in labor input is of greatest importance. This, above all, is the escape route from the dilemma in which governments have found themselves with respect to farm policies. Only when farm incomes become adequate can governments cease to offer price guarantees so high that they induce surplus output (or, where imports are still needed, force the nonfarm population to pay excessive prices for their domestically produced food).

A reduction in labor input of 4 per cent annually and a rise in output of 1.5 per cent per year would increase the value of output

3. Appendix II, Tables A and B; Bureau of the Census, *Statistical Abstract of the United States, 1961*, Washington, 1961.

(at constant prices) by 5.7 per cent per man-year.[4] It would not, however, increase gross product per man-year by that much. Part of the increase would be drained off by a rise in purchased supplies of nonagricultural origin (or imported supplies of agricultural origin). How much this additional cost might be is not easily ascertainable. If the rise in output were limited to 1.5 per cent annually and the amount of land used remained substantially unchanged, very little additional expense per unit of output would be required. Improvement factors of a technological sort which do not represent a charge to the farmer would undoubtedly provide for much of the increased output — better seed and animals, better feeding practices, improved combinations of fertilizers and mineral supplements to the soil, more efficient machinery more fully used. These are all conducive to more output without perceptibly greater outlays by the farmer.

An estimate of the cost of additional supplies of nonagricultural origin in these circumstances is really almost a calculation of the cost of losing labor at a rate of 4 per cent annually. The experience of Sweden indicates that it is very low. While labor input in Sweden was falling by 4 per cent per year the volume of purchased supplies increased by 1 per cent annually and output remained roughly steady.

In Germany, the only other country whose agricultural labor declined by 4 per cent annually in the 1950s, the volume of output rose much more rapidly than the 1.5 per cent per year anticipated in the present model. Hence the experience is somewhat less useful than Sweden's in judging the need for additional purchased supplies to substitute for less labor. If it is reasonable to allocate half the increased volume of current purchases to the increase in output in Germany, the decline of 4 per cent annually in labor input would appear to be associated with a 3 per cent annual rise in purchased materials. In the later years of the 1950s, however, this relation was about 4 per cent to 2 per cent.

In the United States the volume of purchased supplies of nonagricultural origin remained almost stable from 1951 to 1955, out-

---

4. The calculation is correct despite appearances to the contrary.

put rose by 2 per cent a year and labor input dropped by about 3 per cent annually. After the middle of the decade the input of labor continued to decline at the same rate, output rose more rapidly and the volume of purchased supplies increased at a rate of some 3 to 4 per cent annually.

This evidence is far from conclusive, but a rise of 1.5 per cent in output and a fall of 4 per cent in labor input yearly might result in the need for an annual increase of no more than 2 per cent in purchased supplies. The estimate is probably generously high.

To this requirement for additional purchased supplies of non-agricultural origin there must be added depreciation of the physical capital used in agriculture. The figures available on depreciation are rather untrustworthy, viewed from an economic standpoint. In general the estimates of capital depreciation originate from taxation data, and the favorable treatment of farmers by governments extends to depreciation rates which do not in fact reflect the useful life of the capital. There is a wide disparity from one country to another in the reported allowances for depreciation in relation to capital expenditures. However, for the purposes of general estimation of the future in terms of the input-output model described above, it is probably fair to say that depreciation charges might rise by about 3 per cent annually (assuming constant prices for replacement).

Finally, to get at an approximation of profitability of farming under these hypothetical changes in output and costs, it is necessary to make some calculation with respect to hired labor. If man-years of input of hired labor fell at the same rate as those of farm operators and their families — 4 per cent — and wage rates increased by 3 per cent annually (which might reflect growth rates per capita for the entire economy), the wage bill would decline at about 1 per cent a year.

Perhaps this paints too rosy a picture of the outlook for farming in general. After all, only two countries in the region saw declines in labor input of as much as 4 per cent annually during the 1950s. It may be straining the concept of growing productivity to relate increases in output with such a drastic reduction in labor, despite increased purchases of operating supplies and capital at a rate in excess of the expansion of production.

Two estimates are made in Table 12–1. The first is a calculation of the rise in the average farm operator's net income (before allowance for actual or imputed rent and interest) which would result from the input-output model outlined above — 1.5 per cent increase in output, 2 per cent more purchased supplies, 3 per cent more for depreciation and a decline of 3 per cent in labor input (and the number of farm operators), with a rise of 3 per cent annually in wage rates. The second assumes the same factors but reduces the labor input by 4 per cent annually, reducing the wage bill for hired labor as well as lowering more rapidly the number of operators. This hypothetical calculation is for 1970 and is based on farm profits in 1958. (The figure for the base year includes for some countries direct subsidies paid to farmers as well as the "extra" income resulting

Table 12–1. Potential Average Farm Operator Incomes Based on Two Assumptions, Selected Countries, 1970

COUNTRY	ASSUMPTION A		ASSUMPTION B	
	AVERAGE FARM INCOME[a]	PERCENTAGE INCREASE FROM 1958	AVERAGE FARM INCOME[a]	PERCENTAGE INCREASE FROM 1958
Canada	$6,625	56	$7,600	79
U. S.	7,400	46	8,550	69
EEC				
Belgium	6,325	67	7,250	90
France	5,225	102	5,975	131
Germany	4,100	76	4,750	104
Italy	2,600	72	3,000	98
Netherlands	4,850	46	5,625	70
EFTA				
Denmark	5,700	73	6,650	101
Norway	2,075	50	2,375	71
Sweden	2,875	53	3,350	78
U. K.	5,300	25	6,700	59

Sources: Based on Appendix II and Tables 5–1 and 5–2. Both assumptions based on increases in output of 1.5 per cent per year, purchased supplies of 2.0 per cent, capital depreciation allowance of 3.0 per cent; Assumption A based on decline of farm operators and hired labor of 3.0 per cent per year; Assumption B, 4 per cent.
a. Income of farm family, before allowance for interest and rent.

from price-support operations. For others such direct subsidies are excluded.) The price disparities caused by price-support action and other factors in the base year are carried into the calculated values for 1970.[5]

Under the hypothesis of the described changes in farm practices and declining numbers of farmers used in this estimate a reduction of 4 per cent annually would result in a rise of average net income of farm operators (including value of their own labor) between 1958 and 1970 of some 70 to 100 per cent. With a decline in the number of operators and labor of 3 per cent annually, the average would rise by about 45 to 75 per cent. Even if the rest of the economy managed to grow (in terms of net national product per man-year) by 3 per cent annually, or 43 per cent over twelve years, the relative position of farm incomes would be improved in all countries except the United Kingdom, where approximate parity of farm and nonfarm income already exists. In most of them relative farm incomes would reach a degree of parity with nonfarm incomes sufficient to lessen some of the pressure on governments which has led to the present unsatisfactory systems of price and income supports.

FUTURE FARM PRICES

This hypothetical calculation of what farm incomes might be by 1970 is defective, even if its assumptions are correct, to the extent that it employs as a base the price structures prevailing in the individual countries in 1958. If the common agricultural policy of the EEC actually comes into force in 1970 as planned, a unified price structure for agriculture will have been achieved for the six member countries and for those which will have joined the Community by then or will have become associated with it in an effective manner.

Under the arrangements contemplated under the common policy

5. The actual method used was to increase the value of final output at the rate of 1.5 per cent annually and then to deduct from that figure the total cost of purchased supplies, depreciation and wages calculated by the percentage changes shown above. This figure was then reduced to an average per farm by dividing the total by an estimated number of full-time (equivalent) farm operators.

differences in price guarantees and the restrictions on international movement of commodities which are required to enforce those prices will be progressively removed within the Community, while the variable levy and other defenses against outside competition are being erected.

The members of the EEC, in accepting the common policy, conspicuously failed to announce a long-term price policy. For the moment they have put the upper and lower limits of national prices for the interim period at German and French prices, respectively. Until the successive devaluation of the French franc in 1957 and at the end of 1958, French and German farm prices were roughly equal. A wide gap emerged in the comparative price structures in 1959, but was partly closed in the succeeding years as French prices rose more rapidly than German prices. In 1961 French prices were roughly 15 per cent below German prices, a wider margin for cereals and most fruits and vegetables being partly offset by smaller differences for some livestock products. The revaluation of the German mark was also responsible for some of the differences in 1961.

Unless the member countries of the Common Market, and those countries which will probably become members or associates of it, can be persuaded to act otherwise, the ultimate price structure for European agriculture is likely to be one based mainly on prices somewhat higher than French prices now are. Prices would be lower than recent prices in Germany and Italy (and in Sweden, Norway and possibly Austria among the candidates for EEC association), roughly the same as Belgian prices and somewhat higher than recent Dutch (and some British) prices. They would be considerably higher than recent Danish prices.

Such a price structure applied to cereals would put soft wheat at perhaps $90 per ton and feed grains at about $75 per ton — prices which in a number of countries would certainly elicit increases in output which would far outweigh any reduction in output they might bring about in Germany and Italy, where present prices are higher.

What would be the income effects of lower prices for cereals in Europe, such as those proposed in Chapter 11? It is shown there that cereals marketings are not a very large part of total farm revenue in most countries in Western Europe, and it is suggested that prices of $68 for soft wheat and $60 for feed grains, if they continue to be produced and marketed in the same quantities, would nowhere reduce net incomes by more than 9 per cent (Italy) and much less than that in most countries.

In all probability, however, such prices would have the effect of reducing cereals output. This would be particularly true for wheat production in most countries (except feed wheat in those areas in which yields are comparable to those possible for barley and other feed grains). However, it would be easy to overestimate the effect on output of lower prices (even for milling wheat); large economies are possible in cash grain farming as the size of the farm is increased. One almost certain result of a reduction in cereals prices (along with the general exodus from farming) would be more land per farm remaining in cash grain operations.

The decline in production of feed grains might indeed be minor in most countries. On the integrated farm most coarse grain grown is sold in the form of livestock products, particularly as pigs, poultry and eggs. As long as the margin between the prices for these products and feedstuffs is maintained, the absolute price of coarse grains is of little importance to the operators of such farms. Only when the price of purchased feed falls close to production costs and a more profitable use of the land emerges from the lower price structure is feed grain output likely to be curtailed. In general the extent of protection against external competition for livestock products does not exceed that afforded to feed grains.[6] A lower price for cereal feeds might discourage some cash grain farming, but it might well tend to promote integrated farm operation if the margin between feed and livestock prices were widened.

Moreover, even if cereals production were actually reduced by lower prices, the impact on farm income would be mitigated by alternative land use. Modern technology has gone far in the direction of making cattle raising for meat much more intensive and thus more adaptable to European farming conditions.

6. ECE, *Economic Survey of Europe in 1960,* Geneva, 1961, Chap. 3.

In total it is difficult to foresee that lower prices for cereals would provide a serious deterrent to better farm incomes in most countries in Western Europe, though they might bring about some reduction in cash grain farming. The rise in output of 1.5 per cent annually in total agricultural output, assumed in the model constructed above, would come about through an increase in output of livestock products of about 2 per cent, an increase in crop production other than cereals of perhaps 1 per cent and possibly a modest decrease in cereals output.

FUTURE TRADE PATTERNS

The structural model of Western European agriculture outlined above calls for a further concentration of the already considerable effort devoted to raising livestock. To a great extent it is a prescription for action similar to that of many European countries in the field of industry — the importation of relatively low-cost raw materials and their fabrication into higher valued finished products.

This extended effort toward more output of livestock products conforms to the pattern of growth in demand. As shown in Chapter 7, the demand for additional food in Europe will be largely directed toward more livestock products, with particular emphasis on beef and veal. Acceptance of lower prices for cereals would be consistent with raising the density of cattle on the land, whether cattle continued to be mainly dependent on noncereal feedstuffs or were to some extent shifted to cereal feeds.

It is far from certain what this structural shift, if it takes place, will mean for trade in foods and feedstuffs. Much depends on the rapidity with which more farmers in a number of countries in Europe accept and begin to employ changing techniques with respect to growing and feeding noncereal grasses. Very large areas in northern Europe are peculiarly adaptable to growing improved varieties of hay crops, and European farmers are certainly not strangers to grass feeding. However, further advances in economical production and use of these grasses are dependent on adoption of feeding methods which involve considerable capital investment (as well as some specialized knowledge on the part of the livestock producer). High-yielding hay crops will almost certainly provide an attractive alternative to many cereals growers faced with a lower price structure. The effect will be to offset a very large part of any reduction in cereals output which may result from lower prices.

Thus a changed policy with respect to cereals will not bring in its wake a spectacular change in the demand for imports. In all probability, if the policy were put into force over a period of time, it would slow the decline in demand for bread grains from abroad, sustain some rise in coarse grain imports (though not at recent rates of increase) and reduce the imports of butter and meat. A variation of that pattern would occur if the cereals price reductions, which could bring wheat prices down more than those for feed grains, had the effect of shifting growers from wheat to coarse grains. In that event wheat imports might well increase somewhat, but this would be offset by a relative decline in coarse grain purchases from abroad.

IS THIS MODEL PRACTICAL?

The pattern of European agriculture described above, to be achieved over a period of a decade, calls for a gradual structural change in the direction of more concentration on final agricultural products. In effect, it suggests that Europe forgo to some extent its present politically pleasant but economically expensive objective of providing virtually all of its needs for bread grains and the raw materials for its livestock industry.

The implications for the North Atlantic and Australasian suppliers are complementary to those for European agriculturalists. If the latter, through their governments' policies, are to be expected to acquiesce in a pattern of production and trade which ends expansion of cereals growing in parts of Europe (and perhaps leads to a diminution), their governments should be able to say without equivocation that cereals are being obtained from abroad at unsubsidized prices which cannot be met by many producers in Europe. Put bluntly, external suppliers of Europe's cereals needs can hope to retain their market only if they can demonstrate their competitive superiority by ending their subsidization of cereals production and exports. The point is most applicable to the United States, but Australia and Canada have shown increasing tendencies toward various forms of subsidization.

The responsibility for making the first move toward this objective thus lies with the supplying countries, in particular the United States. The opportunity — indeed, the unavoidable point in time — for making this move arises with British entry into the EEC. That event, if it finally takes place, will be marked by a commitment by the United Kingdom to bring its production, pricing and trading policies for cereals into line with those of the Common Market. There will, of course, be a period of adjustment. However, the basic lines of the ultimate arrangement with respect to the future pattern of production and trade in cereals will be drawn at that time.

At that point, and for a protracted period after it, American negotiators and those from other supplying countries must be able to come to the conference table armed with assurances that they can supply Europe with cereals at relatively low prices, such as those suggested in Chapter 11, and that, at the end of a transition period, those prices will be unsubsidized. To be able to say this will not assure that the cereals trade will be salvaged from the autarkic plans of the Common Market now in prospect. Inability to say it, however, will almost automatically foreclose any chance of Europe's adopting a less illiberal policy objective than that which it now has in mind. The voices of those in Europe — not few in number — who have an interest in a reasonably low price structure for food and whose interest in this circumstance coincides with foreign suppliers of cereals to Europe will be substantially muted unless they can say that Europe will be forgoing an important competitive advantage if it refuses low-cost cereals from abroad — and say that without raising the cry of "subsidies" and "dumping" from the supporters of high prices for European farmers.

Can assurances of no subsidies and low prices be made? Table 11–2 estimated the impact of a lower cereals price structure on farm incomes in a number of countries. The dimensions of that problem raised by such a change in prices do not appear insuperably great, even in the United States, where the prices of cereals are highest among the main supplying countries. With fuller understanding that continuation of subsidization can contribute much to a decline in the market for cereals in Europe in the next few years, some legislators, especially in the U. S. Congress, may perhaps be persuaded of the wisdom of getting away from, and perhaps finally abandoning, high price supports as the method of attempting to support incomes of grain farmers.

IS IT WORTH TRYING?

If some economic sense is restored to the cereals market in the North Atlantic region, it can probably be classed as one of the minor political miracles of this period. But these are times of political miracles, minor and major. The economic unification of most of Western Europe, which brings immediacy to the problem of the cereals trade as one of its less important by-products, is a major political development deserving superlative description. The free world is going through a period in which it is dangerous to discard ideas for change on the grounds of "political impossibility."

Nevertheless, it could be argued that bringing some economic order into national cereals policies and international trade is scarcely worth the candle. Nowhere in the industrialized world are cereals production and trade of great economic importance in terms of total national economies. Moreover, the magnitude of the shifts which would be involved in locating marginal production in the more productive areas is not so great as to make any fundamental economic difference to any country in the region, whether it gains or loses in the redistributive process.

The answer to the question perhaps verges on the philosophical. It is probably fair to say that agriculture is the "rotten borough" of modern politico-economic democracy in industrialized economies. We can, of course, be thankful that the agricultural problems of the West are what they are rather than those faced by Eastern Europe, the Soviet Union, China and much of the rest of the world. The embarrassment of plenty is certainly to be preferred to the disaster of hunger.

That attribute, however, is not a sufficient justification for maintaining agriculture in its present state or for blocking an adjustment process which can and should be supported by public action. The economic waste involved in present agricultural policies, if not precisely measurable, can be seen to be considerable. But it is the low-grade political infection carried by farm politics which should be of real concern to Western democracies. There are few legislative bodies in which the blatant vote trading engaged in by farmers' representatives can be matched by spokesmen for other organized groups. Few other groups use the political bludgeon in support of special interests so sweepingly and with such skill.

It is true, of course, that "farming is different." There is no suggestion here that governments can, or should, cease to exercise a protective force in favor of the farmer in his economic relations with the rest of society. In the modern industrial economy as it has evolved, true competitors are as out of place and as much in need of special treatment as are true monopolists. Having recognized that fact, governments must then act reasonably in meting out their special treatment. Reasonableness in this context means bringing about economic results which are similar to those which would have obtained had the competitors or the monopolists in fact been subjected to the sort of quasi-competition which marks the rest of the economy. The further this standard is departed from, the more pernicious the politics of special treatment is likely to become.

It is submitted here that most governments have departed rather considerably from this standard in dealing with agriculture. They should, in an interest which is broader than economics alone, act to rectify their errors. Cereals is a good segment to start on. And if the job can be done in an international context, so much the better.

APPENDIX I

Population

Estimated End-of-Year Population, by Country, 1950, 1955 and 1960, and Projections for 1970 and 1980   (*Thousands*)

COUNTRY	1950	1955	1960	1970	1980
Canada	13,861	15,919	18,040	22,000	26,000
U. S.	153,072	166,818	181,500[a]	215,000	254,000
EEC	156,013	162,151	170,025	182,000	193,500
BLEU	8,953	9,207	9,500	10,000	10,500
France	41,910	43,442	45,725	49,000	53,000
Germany	48,182	50,495	53,750	56,250	59,000
Italy	46,768	48,185	49,500	54,000	57,000
Netherlands	10,200	10,822	11,550	12,750	14,000
EFTA	85,173	87,298	90,120	94,600	100,000
Austria	6,932	6,977	7,100	7,200	7,300
Denmark	4,289	4,454	4,600	4,900	5,200
Norway	3,280	3,446	3,600	3,900	4,200
Portugal	8,441	8,801	9,160	9,900	10,700
Sweden	7,042	7,290	7,500	8,000	8,500
Switzerland	4,715	5,004	5,410	5,800	6,400
U. K.	50,474	51,326	52,750	54,900	57,700

Sources: 1950, 1955 and 1960 (estimated) — OEEC, *General Statistics,* Paris, January 1961; projections for 1970 and 1980 are based partly on unpublished OEEC data and U. S. Bureau of the Census estimates and on extrapolation of population trends in Canada, assuming somewhat reduced immigration compared to recent years.

a. Excludes Alaska and Hawaii.

Agricultural Land, Labor, Value and Costs

LAND (TABLE A)

Sources: The basic data on land utilized for agricultural purposes were taken from OEEC, *Agricultural and Food Statistics*, Paris, 1959. This was supplemented by statistics from FAO, *Production Yearbook, 1958* and *1960*, Rome, 1959 and 1961; ECE, *Economic Survey of Europe in 1960*, Geneva, 1961, Chap. 3 and appendix material related to that chapter; USDA, *Agricultural Statistics, 1957, 1959,* and *1960*, Washington, 1958, 1960 and 1961.

Comparability of Data: National systems of land classification vary. The OEEC utilized national statistics in the source cited above, but could not assure complete comparability. The classification system used divided agricultural land into "arable land," which is subdivided into "tillage" and "temporary grassland," "permanent grassland," and "rough grazings." No use is made in this volume of the last class of land. However, data for Portugal include rough grazings with permanent grassland.

An adjustment in land-use data for the United States was made to eliminate land used for production of cotton and tobacco in those chapters of this volume which deal with food and feedstuff production. No comparable adjustment was made for other countries, in most of which the amount of land used for industrial crops is very minor.

LABOR (TABLE B)

Sources: The chief sources used for the estimates of labor utilized in agriculture are included in those listed above for land use, plus ECE/FAO, *Output, Expenses and Income of Agriculture in European Countries,* Third and Fourth Reports, Geneva, 1958 and 1961; ILO, *Why Labour Leaves the Land*, Geneva, 1960; ILO, *Year Book of Labour Statistics, 1959*, Geneva, 1960; OEEC, *Agricultural Policies in Europe and*

North America, Second and Fifth Reports, Paris, 1957 and 1961; ECE/FAO, *European Agriculture in 1965,* Geneva, 1961, mimeo.

Comparability of Data: In order to estimate "man-years devoted to agriculture," the author has attempted to adjust part-time work in agriculture to a full-time basis for farm workers with other occupations as well as farming but to exclude time lost through involuntary unemployment of persons predominantly engaged in agriculture. However, the basic data on which these calculations are made are extremely varied. In some European countries and the United States there are numerous statistical series: active population in agriculture, employment status and man-hours worked. In most other countries only the first two measures are available, though in some a measure of man-years is attempted. National census definitions vary widely and intercensal reporting differs in depth and scope as well as in definition. Thus, the labor estimates made in this volume are of limited reliability, particularly with respect to international comparisons.

VALUE AND COSTS (TABLES C, D, E AND F)

Sources: The primary sources for this material are ECE/FAO, *Output, Expenses and Income of Agriculture in European Countries,* Third and Fourth Reports, Geneva, 1958 and 1961, together with some of the basic data collected for the fourth report made available by ECE/FAO to the author; USDA, *Agricultural Statistics, 1960,* and preceding years, Washington, 1961, and preceding years; and Dominion Bureau of Statistics, *Quarterly Bulletin of Agricultural Statistics,* Ottawa, various issues.

Exchange Rates: The exchange rates used to convert national currencies to dollars are the following: Canada (dollar), $1.00; Belgium-Luxembourg (franc), $0.02; France (old franc), $0.00238, unless otherwise noted; Germany (mark), $0.238; Italy (lira), $0.0016; Netherlands (guilder), $0.263; Austria (schilling), $0.0385; Denmark (krone), $0.145; Norway (krone), $0.14; Portugal (escudo), $0.03475; Sweden (krona), $0.193; Switzerland (franc), $0.233; United Kingdom (pound), $2.80. (See also section on exchange rates in "Notes and Abbreviations.")

Rounding: All value estimates have been rounded to nearest 5 or zero. Constant price calculations are based on various data given in above sources. Although 1951 is used here as the base year, constant price indexes in the sources were based on various years, usually two to four years in the late 1940s or early 1950s.

Comparability of Data: Treatment of changes in inventories is not consistent from country to country. For most countries, however, it appears that adjustments for inventory changes have been made. Similarly, the treatment of indirect taxes and subsidies is not entirely consistent. Apparently indirect taxes in most countries are included in the value of current purchases, while subsidies attributable to price support are sometimes included in the value of output. Where the difference between value of output and value of purchases does not equal gross agricultural product, the difference is due to separate treatment of subsidies or indirect taxes or both.

Comparable data for Switzerland and Portugal are not available. Partial information indicates that their inclusion would increase most of the EFTA totals by about 20 per cent.

For Denmark value data include net revenues from operation of dairies and slaughterhouses.

Table A. Agricultural Land Utilization, by Country, Mid–1950s

COUNTRY	THOUSAND HECTARES			PER CENT OF ARABLE LAND			
	ALL AGRI-CULTURAL LAND[a]	PERMANENT PASTURE	ARABLE LAND	TEMPORARY GRASS	ALL CROPS	CEREALS	POTATOES AND SUGAR BEETS
Canada	61,216	26,070	35,146	...	...	52.6	0.5
U.S.	374,320	212,860	161,460	16.6	83.4	49.1	0.6
EEC	69,484	21,644	47,840	12.5	87.5	45.5	8.0
BLEU	1,876	787	1,089	5.5	94.5	51.7	14.0
France	34,069	12,773	21,296	25.4	74.6	41.7	6.7
Germany	14,250	5,596	8,654	2.6	97.4	55.6	16.2
Italy	16,979	1,230	15,749	18.6	81.4	44.5	3.9
Netherlands	2,310	1,258	1,052	3.7	96.3	49.7	20.4
EFTA	29,502	8,716	20,786	34.8[b]	65.2[b]	44.0	6.2
Austria	2,858	1,091	1,767	26.0	74.0	49.9	12.5
Denmark	3,047	304	2,743	25.2	74.8	49.5	5.8
Norway	1,013	185	828	62.6	37.4	23.3	6.8
Portugal	4,940[c]	810[c]	4,130	...	...	46.8	2.1
Sweden	3,884	187	3,697	40.3	59.7	41.0	4.7
Switzerland	1,191	744	447	36.7	63.3	38.9	14.3
U.K.	12,569	5,395	7,174	34.5	65.5	43.2	7.5

Source: OEEC, *Agricultural and Food Statistics*, Paris, 1959.
a. Excludes rough grazing areas.   b. Excludes Portugal.   c. Includes Portugal.   c. Includes rough grazing areas.

Table B. Estimated Number of Man-Years of Labor Input in Agriculture, by Country, 1951, 1955 and 1958

(Thousands)

COUNTRY	1951	1955	1958			
			TOTAL	BY FARM OPERATORS	BY OPERATORS AND OTHER FAMILY MEMBERS	BY HIRED WORKERS
Canada	850	750	660	375	560	100
U.S.	6,600	6,000	5,300	3,000	4,200	1,100
EEC	(15,310)	(14,060)	13,175	(5,625)	(10,370)	2,805
BLEU[a]	(345)	(300)	(265)	(165)	(220)	(45)
France	4,050	3,800	3,600	1,800	3,000	600
Germany	3,600	3,000	2,700	1,100	2,100	600
Italy	6,800	6,480	6,150	2,350	4,700	1,450
Netherlands	515	480	460	210	350	110
EFTA[b]	(3,160)	(2,870)	(2,705)	...	...	...
Austria	715	700	670	...	...	...
Denmark	395	350	325	170	210	105
Norway	245	215	200	130	180	20
Portugal	...	(1,300)	...	...	...	...
Sweden	450	365	340	210	275	65
Switzerland	(300)	(280)	(265)	...	...	...
U.K.	1,055	960	905	260	300	605

Sources: See preceding text.   b. Excludes Portugal.
a. Belgium comprises about 90 per cent.

Table C. Value of Agricultural Output at Current and Constant Prices by Country, 1951, 1955 and 1958

COUNTRY	CURRENT PRICES (MILLIONS)			CONSTANT PRICES (INDEX: 1951 = 100)		
	1951	1955	1958	1951	1955	1958
Canada[a]	$ 3,590	$ 2,925	$ 3,130	100	(96)	(93)
U. S.[a]	36,600	31,660	36,280	100	109	119
EEC	14,575	17,360	20,680	100	114	125
Belgium	875	945	1,020	100	117	128
France	4,725	5,785	7,590	100	117	123
Germany	3,865	4,385	5,295	100	108	123
Italy	4,095	5,015	5,410	100	115	127
Netherlands	1,015	1,230	1,365	100	118	129
EFTA	5,430	6,645	7,195	100	(110)	(120)
Austria	515	725	785	100	121	124
Denmark	875	1,020	1,080	100	(110)	(128)
Norway	240	325	370	100	111	120
Sweden	700	750	815	100	93	97
U. K.[a]	(3,100)	3,825	4,145	(100)	(112)	(123)

Sources: See preceding text.

a. Based on sum of farm marketings and human consumption on farms. Therefore the figure includes certain kinds of "interfarm transactions." For the United States such transactions (feed grains, seed and livestock) were valued by the seller at about $4.5 billion in 1951, $4.2 billion in 1955 and $5.5 billion in 1958. For Canada (feed grains and seed only) the comparable figures are estimated at approximately $200 million in 1951 and 1955, $225 million in 1958. For the United Kingdom the figures are not known, but were apparently a very small part of total output.

Table D.   Value of Purchases of Current Operating Supplies at Current and Constant Prices, by Country, 1951, 1955 and 1958

COUNTRY	CURRENT PRICES (MILLIONS)			CONSTANT PRICES (INDEX: 1951 = 100)		
	1951	1955	1958	1951	1955	1958
Canada[a]	$ (790)	$ (950)	$(1,075)	(100)	(117)	(123)
U. S.[a]	13,500	12,795	15,380	100	99	113
EEC	3,060	3,950	4,940	100	129	151
Belgium	275	310	340	100	102	107
France	935	1,200	1,665	100	136	162
Germany	980	1,280	1,600	100	129	152
Italy	535	710	805	100	129	149
Netherlands	335	450	530	100	136	160
EFTA	1,925	2,715	3,020			
Austria	130	195	210	100	115	119
Denmark	215	280	295	(100)	(114)	(125)
Norway	65	95	115	100	131	142
Sweden	195	260	270	100	119	112
U. K.[a]	1,320	1,885	2,130	(100)	(125)	(142)

Sources: See preceding text.

a. Includes value of purchases of goods of agricultural origin originating on other farms within national boundaries. For the United States the values, to the buyers, were about $6.5 billion in 1951, $5.5 billion in 1955 and $7 billion in 1958. In Canada the figures (feedstuff and seed only) were probably about $275 million in 1951 and 1955 and about $300 million in 1958. The figures for the United Kingdom are unknown but were undoubtedly small.

These estimates differ from those shown in the footnote to Table C because they include costs of handling between the farm of origin and the buyer, the value of feedstuffs bought back (bran, oilseed residues and skim milk) and the costs of converting domestically produced feedstuffs into mixed feeds.

Table E. Gross Agricultural Product (at Factor Cost)[a] at Current and Constant Prices, by Country, 1951, 1955 and 1958

COUNTRY	CURRENT PRICES (MILLIONS)			CONSTANT PRICES (INDEX: 1951 = 100)		
	1951	1955	1958	1951	1955	1958
Canada	$ 2,800	$ 1,975	$ 2,055	100	91	86
U. S.	23,400	19,100	21,980	100	124	125
EEC[b]	11,435	13,355	15,830	100	110	118
Belgium	595	630	680	100	128	140
France	3,790	4,590	5,920	100	112	114
Germany	2,825	3,050	3,695	100	101	113
Italy	3,565	4,310	4,605	100	112	124
Netherlands	660	775	930	100	109	114
EFTA[b]	3,645	4,125	4,420	100	105	113
Austria	385	525	570	100	124	126
Denmark	(670)	755	800	100	107	127
Norway	185	240	260	100	104	112
Sweden	535	515	575	100	82	91
U. K.	1,870	2,090	2,215	(100)	(107)	(112)

Sources: See preceding text.
a. At market prices for France, Italy and Denmark.
b. For countries listed.

Table F. Gross Fixed Capital Formation and Depreciation, by Country, 1951, 1955 and 1958   (*Millions*)

COUNTRY	CAPITAL FORMATION			DEPRECIATION		
	1951	1955	1958	1951	1955	1958
Canada	. . .	. . .	. . .	$ 195	$ 285	$ 285
U. S.	$4,825	$4,230	$4,525	3,225	3,720	3,960
EEC	1,170	1,680	2,080	765	1,010	1,340
Belgium	50ª	65	60	35	50	50
France	315	460	655	(215)	(320)	(475)
Germany	315	475	630	195	240	360
Italy	425	595	660	275	345	395
Netherlands	65	85	75	45	55	60
EFTA	510	600	725	310	425	515
Austria	60	130	160	35	70	90
Denmarkᵇ	60ª	45	50	40	45	55
Norway	50	65	70	35	50	60
Sweden	80	80	85	50	65	80
U. K.	260	280	360	150	195	230

Sources: See preceding text; capital formation for Denmark, OEEC, *General Statistics,* Paris, March 1961.
    a. 1953.   b. Includes dairies and slaughterhouses.

APPENDIX III

Consumption and Production

Sources: FAO, Rome — *Production Yearbook, 1958* and *1960,* 1959 and 1961; *Monthly Bulletin of Agricultural Economics and Statistics,* various issues. OEEC, Paris — *Agricultural and Food Statistics,* 1959; *Agriculture: Production and Consumption Figures,* 1961; *General Statistics,* various issues.

Methods: "Wheat equivalent" has been used in this study as a quantity unit for production, output and consumption to express aggregates of different commodities. The weights applied to each of the major products are shown in the tabulation below. They reflect average European prices to the producer in the period 1952–1956. They are based on, but depart slightly from, those shown in two publications: ECE/FAO, *European Agriculture in 1965,* Geneva, 1960, mimeo.; and FAO, *Monthly Bulletin,* Rome, March 1960.

Weights Used in Aggregating Production and Consumption Totals in Terms of Wheat Equivalent*

Production		Consumption	
Product	*Weight*	*Product*	*Weight*
Bread grains	1.00 ⎫	Cereals as flour or	
Rice	1.00 ⎬	milled rice	1.33
Coarse grains	0.85		
Potatoes	0.33	Potatoes	0.33
Sugar (raw)	1.10	Sugar (refined)	1.20
Olive oil	4.40 ⎫	Fats (exc. butter but	
Oilseeds	1.75 ⎬	inc. slaughter fats	
		& marine oils)	4.80
Pulses	1.45	Pulses, fruits and	
Fruit	0.90	vegetables	0.90
Vegetables	0.50		
Wine	0.85	**	**
Meat (dressed		Meat (dressed	
carcass weight)	7.40	carcass weight)	7.40
Eggs	8.15	Eggs	8.15
Milk	0.80	Milk (and products	
		as milk)	0.80

* For special calculations for milk products and for "standard" meat, see Table A, footnotes b and c.

** Wine excluded from consumption index.

This method of aggregation was used in making consumption estimates in Chapter 6, Tables 6–6 and 6–7. The same method with a modification in the evaluation of meat (see the final column and footnote "c" on Table A) was used in making the estimates and projections in Table D. (Attention is also called to footnote "b" on Table A, which defines a standard milk used in this appendix as well as in Tables 6–6 and 6–7.)

The same method, using the production weights, was used in making the aggregate food production and output estimates shown in Tables E and F. They were also employed in Chapter 8, Tables 8–4, 8–5 and 8–6 for trade as well as production, output and utilization estimates.

Table A. Estimated Average Annual Per Capita Consumption of Major Food Groups, 1954–1956

(Kilograms)

COUNTRY	CEREALS (AS FLOUR)	POTA- TOES	SUGAR	FRUITS, NUTS, VEGE- TABLES AND PULSES	FATS (EXC. BUTTER)[a]	MEAT	MILK AND MILK PROD- UCTS[b]	EGGS	MEAT (STAND- ARD)[c]
Canada	74	68	44	140	12.1	81	333	16	87.1
U. S.	69	49	41	(200)[d]	17.4	92	276	21	88.3
EEC	114.4	113.1	24.7	150	15.2	46.2	198	9.5	41.2
BLEU	100	150	29	142	12.8	52	254	14	53.4
France	111	130	26	180	11.2	74	236	10	66.0
Germany	96	158	28	114	19.5	48	238	10	46.0
Italy	145	48	16	168	12.4	20	102	8	14.5
Netherlands	90	96	39	121	25.1	38	244	8	27.8

Continued on following page

Table A (continued)

COUNTRY	CEREALS (AS FLOUR)	POTATOES	SUGAR	FRUITS, NUTS, VEGETABLES AND PULSES	FATS (EXC. BUTTER)[a]	MEAT	MILK AND MILK PRODUCTS[b]	EGGS	MEAT (STANDARD)[c]
EFTA	94.4	101.5	41.2	114	16.0	57.4	252	10.7	64.5
Austria	118	96	31	123	14.0	47	238	8	43.1
Denmark	90	131	48	119	18.9	63	284	8	72.3
Norway	98	108	38	71	25.0	36	315	8	33.2
Portugal	125	113	15	176	15.0	17	28	3	16.9
Sweden	76	102	42	88	13.1	52	377	10	54.6
Switzerland	101	83	38	166	12.0	51	331	10	50.0
U.K.	88	99	47	104	16.4	68	260	13	79.8

Sources: FAO, *Production Yearbook, 1958*, Rome, 1959; OEEC, *Agricultural and Food Statistics*, Paris, 1959.

a. Fat content. Includes slaughter fats and marine oils, which account for about 30 to 40 per cent in most countries.

b. Includes butter. Caloric value of the products converted to kg. of fluid milk with 3.9 per cent fat and caloric value of 680 calories per kg.

c. Caloric value of meat converted to kilograms at rate of 2,375 calories per kg. This is used as basis for projections in Tables B, C and D.

d. Estimate. Source excludes canned and frozen vegetables.

Table B. Estimated Caloric Value of Daily Per Capita Food Consumption and Percentage Derived from Vegetable Products and Livestock Products, by Country, Annual Average, 1954–1956, and Projections for 1970 and 1980

| | CALORIES PER DAY | | | PERCENTAGE DISTRIBUTION BY TYPE OF PRODUCT | | | | | | | | |
| | | | | 1954–1956 | | | 1970 | | | 1980 | | |
COUNTRY	1954–1956	1970	1980	TOTAL[a]	VEGE-TABLE	LIVE-STOCK	TOTAL[a]	VEGE-TABLE	LIVE-STOCK	TOTAL[a]	VEGE-TABLE	LIVE-STOCK
Canada	3,150	3,100	3,100	99	54	45	99	53	46	99	53	46
U.S.	3,150	3,100	3,100	99	56	43	99	54	45	99	53	46
EEC	2,830	2,970	3,070	99	72	27	99	68	31	99	63	36
BLEU	2,970	3,000	3,100	96	63	33	97	61	36	98	58	40
France	2,890	3,000	3,100	99	69	30	99	64	35	99	60	39
Germany	2,990	3,000	3,100	99	68	31	99	64	35	99	60	39
Italy	2,550	2,900	3,000	99	84	15	99	78	21	99	70	29
Netherlands	2,940	3,000	3,100	96	70	26	97	66	31	98	62	36
EFTA	3,120	3,020	3,070	97	64	33	98	62	36	98	59	39
Austria	2,900	3,000	3,100	100	67	33	100	64	36	100	62	38
Denmark	3,360	3,100	3,100	97	63	34	97	61	36	98	58	40
Norway	3,160	3,000	3,100	87	58	29	89	58	31	91	58	33
Portugal	2,450	2,600	2,800	97	83	14	97	80	17	97	75	22
Sweden	2,980	3,000	3,100	96	59	37	97	58	39	98	57	41
Switzerland	3,130	3,000	3,100	100	67	33	100	63	37	100	60	40
U.K.	3,260	3,100	3,100	97	61	36	98	59	39	98	57	41

Sources: 1954–1956 — FAO, *Production Yearbook, 1960,* Rome, 1961. Data have been revised to include butter and slaughter fats with livestock products. 1970 and 1980 projections are estimates based on Table C.

a. Components do not necessarily add to 100 because of the exclusion of fish and fish oils.

Table C.   Estimated Average Annual Per Capita Consumption of
Major Food Groups, by Area, 1970 and 1980   (*Kilograms*)

FOOD GROUP	CANADA		U. S.		EEC		EFTA	
	1970	1980	1970	1980	1970	1980	1970	1980
Cereals (as flour)	62	56	62	56	85	75	74	64
Sugar	44	44	44	44	41	43	42	43
Other vegetable foods								
Potatoes	55	40	45	40	90	85	80	70
Fruit & vegetables	160	170	195	200	180	185	140	165
Vegetable oils (fat)	8	11	10	11	10	12	11	11
Meat and eggs								
Meat[a]	96	100	94	100	51	59	72	82
Eggs	19	19	19	19	14	17	14	17
Slaughter fats	7	8	9	9	5	7	4	5
Milk (and milk products as milk)	300	275	260	260	225	265	250	265

Source: Estimated by author.
a. See meat (standard) in Table A.

Table D. Estimated Average Annual Food Consumption, by Area, 1954–1956, 1970 and 1980   *(Wheat Equivalent)*

AREA	1954–1956	1970	1980
	PER CAPITA, KG.		
Canada	1,400	1,475	1,500
U. S.	1,465	1,475	1,520
EEC	970	1,100	1,225
EFTA	1,155	1,225	1,345
	TOTAL, MILLION TONS		
Canada	22.3	32.5	39.0
U. S.	244.4	317.1	388.1
EEC	157.3ª	200.2	237.0
EFTA	100.8	115.9	134.5
	TOTAL, INDEX: 1954–1956 = 100		
Canada	100	146	175
U. S.	100	130	159
EEC	100	127	151
EFTA	100	115	133

Sources: Tables A and C and tabulation in preceding text showing weights; population increase from Appendix I.

a. Differs from total shown in Tables 8–4 and 8–5, mainly because of exclusion of wine from consumption index and difference in period used for production and output data in those tables.

Table E. Production[a] of Food and Feedstuffs, by Country, Annual Average, 1953–1957   (*Million Tons, Wheat Equivalent*)

			LIVESTOCK	
COUNTRY	TOTAL	CROPS	AMOUNT	PER CENT OF LIVE-STOCK PRODUCTS FROM IMPORTED FEEDSTUFFS
Canada	45.9	28.1	17.8	—
U. S.	371.6	179.9	191.7	—
EEC	211.7	99.0	112.7	8
BLEU	11.5	3.8	7.7	27
France	77.7	34.5	43.2	2
Germany[b]	(60.4)	(25.9)	(34.5)	9
Italy	46.4	30.1	16.3	4
Netherlands	15.7	4.7	11.0	20
EFTA	93.4	34.1	59.3	16
Austria	8.9	3.8	5.1	10
Denmark	16.6	5.4	11.2	13
Norway	3.5	0.9	2.6	19
Portugal	5.8	4.5	1.3	—
Sweden	11.0	4.4	6.6	7
Switzerland	5.8	1.5	4.3	9
U. K.	41.8	13.6	28.2	22

Sources: OEEC, Paris: *Agricultural and Food Statistics,* 1959; and *Agriculture,* 1961. See preceding text for method.

a. Inclusion of production of tobacco, vegetable fibers and wool would increase totals by 8 per cent in the United States and by 1 per cent in Canada and Europe.

b. Includes estimate for the Saar.

Table F. Total and Per Capita Output[a] of Food and Feed Crops and Livestock Products, by Country, Annual Average, 1953–1957 *(Wheat Equivalent)*

COUNTRY	TOTAL OUTPUT (MILLION TONS)			PER CAPITA OUTPUT, KG.		
	ALL ITEMS	CROPS	LIVE-STOCK PRODUCTS	ALL ITEMS	CROPS	LIVE-STOCK PRODUCTS
Canada	33.7	16.1	17.6	2,120	1,010	1,110
U. S.	292.3	103.2	189.1	1,750	620	1,130
EEC	169.9	66.2	103.7	1,050	410	640
BLEU	9.6	2.6	7.0	1,040	280	760
France	63.2	23.0	40.2	1,450	530	920
Germany[b]	43.0	11.8	31.2	870	240	630
Italy	40.3	25.6	14.7	830	530	300
Netherlands	13.8	3.2	10.6	1,280	300	980
EFTA	75.4	19.2	56.2	860	220	640
Austria	6.7	2.2	4.5	960	310	650
Denmark	12.3	1.8	10.5	2,760	400	2,360
Norway	2.8	0.4	2.4	810	120	690
Portugal	5.2	3.9	1.3	590	440	150
Sweden	8.5	2.3	6.2	1,150	300	850
Switzerland	4.8	1.0	3.8	960	200	760
U. K.	35.1	7.6	27.5	680	150	530

Sources: OEEC, *Agricultural and Food Statistics,* Paris, 1959; *General Statistics,* March and May, 1961; and Appendix I.

a. Inclusion of output of tobacco, vegetable fibers and wool would increase totals by 10 per cent in the United States and by less than 2 per cent in Canada and Europe.

b. Excludes the Saar.

NOTES AND ABBREVIATIONS

A number of terms, conventions and abbreviations used in this study are explained below.

GENERAL NOTES

Geographical Terms

"Atlantic community," "area" or "region" has been used to include the six members of the EEC, the seven members of the EFTA, Canada and the United States. (See EEC and EFTA under "International Agencies and Associations.") Conceptually, although not geographically, Australia and New Zealand (and sometimes Argentina and Uruguay) are parts of this "region" for most purposes, although they are not included statistically in this study unless specifically named. Their importance should be kept in mind, however, as parts of the main area exporting nontropical foods to Europe. Japan is "North Atlantic" in the sense of being industrialized and an importer of nontropical foods on a commercial basis.

"Britain" is used interchangeably with "the United Kingdom" which means all of the British Isles except the Republic of Ireland.

"Europe" and "Western Europe," unless otherwise defined, are used interchangeably to mean the thirteen European countries included in this survey: Austria, Belgium, Denmark, France, Germany (Federal Republic), Italy, Luxembourg, the Netherlands, Norway, Portugal, Sweden, Switzerland, and the United Kingdom. These European countries were selected because they include the six members of the EEC and the seven members of the EFTA (see EEC and EFTA below under "International Agencies and Associations") and as such have taken the initial steps toward economic integration. Spain, Greece, Ireland and Iceland could have been included in "Europe" but generally have not been.

"Germany" means the German Federal Republic. Though the Saar is now a part of the Federal Republic, figures shown in this study for Germany usually exclude the Saar, unless otherwise indicated. This is necessary for comparability of data, since full economic integration of the Saar with the Federal Republic was not achieved until the end of 1959.

"North America" as used in this study includes Canada and the United States.

Prices

Unless otherwise indicated, all dollar figures are in U. S. dollars at official exchange rates and at current prices.

Dates

A year written thus — 1959/60 — usually represents a crop year in this study and is a twelve-month period covering parts of the two calendar years indicated. On the other hand "1959–1960" means two full years. In many instances references pertaining to agricultural statistics simply follow the systems used by the agencies which collect the statistics — whether for calendar years or crop years. When a single year is given — 1958, for example — some of the data are for the crop year 1958/59. For such split years, the year shown is the earlier of the two.

ABBREVIATIONS

The following is a listing of the short forms and abbreviations (other than those given below under "Weights and Measures" and "Foreign Exchange Rates") used generally in this study.

National and International Agencies and Associations

Benelux
   A limited customs union composed of Belgium, the Netherlands and Luxembourg.

BLEU
   Belgium-Luxembourg Economic Union, virtually a complete economic union of the two countries.

Common Market
   See EEC.

Community, the
   See EEC.

ECE
   The Economic Commission for Europe, established under the Economic and Social Council of the United Nations, with headquarters in Geneva.

ECE/FAO
   The combined office of the Food and Agriculture Organization and the ECE Agriculture Division in Geneva.

EEC

> The European Economic Community, also known as "the Common Market," "the Community," and "the Six." Member countries are Belgium, the Netherlands, Luxembourg, the Federal Republic of Germany, France and Italy.

EFTA

> European Free Trade Association, also called "the Outer Seven." Member countries are Austria, Denmark, Norway, Portugal, Sweden, Switzerland and the United Kingdom.

FAO

> The Food and Agricultural Organization, a specialized agency of the United Nations. Headquarters in Rome.

GATT

> The General Agreement on Tariffs and Trade, an agreement between most of the noncommunist nations with substantial interest in foreign trade formed for the purpose of negotiating changes in tariff rates and quota restrictions. Headquarters in Geneva.

HMSO

> Her Majesty's Stationery Office, official publisher for the Government of the United Kingdom.

OECD

> See OEEC.

OEEC

> Organisation for European Economic Cooperation, organized in 1948 by the signatories of the Convention for European Economic Cooperation to deal on a centralized basis with the work of the "Marshall Plan" (International Cooperation Act), known in Europe as the European Recovery Program (ERP) and administered from the side of the United States by the Economic Cooperation Administration (ECA) and successor agencies. Members of the OEEC were Austria, Belgium, Denmark, France, Germany, Greece, Iceland, Ireland, Italy, Luxembourg, the Netherlands, Norway, Portugal, Sweden, Switzerland, Turkey, the United Kingdom, and after 1959, Spain. Yugoslavia was represented by an observer. The United States and Canada were associate members. The OEEC was succeeded in September 1961 by the Organisation for Economic Cooperation and Development (OECD), with the members listed above, but with the United States and Canada as full members.

USDA

> United States Department of Agriculture, Washington, D.C.

Technical Terms

c.i.f.

"Cost, insurance and freight," a term denoting that a given figure includes, in addition to the value of the merchandise shipped, the insurance paid on it and the carrier's charges. It is normally used interchangeably with "landed cost."

f.o.b.

"Free on board," a term denoting that a given figure includes only the value of merchandise loaded on the carrier, and excludes insurance and carrier costs.

ha.

hectare, see "Weights and Measures."

kg.

kilogram, see "Weights and Measures."

WEIGHTS AND MEASURES

Unless otherwise specified, the metric system of weights and measures has been used in this study. The following table gives the American and English equivalents of the most common of these measures used here and the abbreviations commonly employed.

Weights

1 kilogram (kg.)	2.20456 pounds
100 grams	3.52 ounces
1 ounce	28.35 grams
1 metric ton (m.t.) (used interchangeably with ton)	2,204.56 pounds, or 36.74 bushels (wheat), or 1.102 short tons (U. S.), or 0.984 long tons (British)
1 pound (lb.)	0.4536 kg.
1 short ton	0.9072 m.t., or 907.2 kg.
1 long ton	1.0161 m.t., or 1,016.1 kg.
1 bushel (wheat)	60 pounds, 27.2 kg.

Square Measures

1 hectare (ha.)	10,000 m.^{2}, or 2.4711 acres
1 acre	4,047 m.^{2}, or 0.4047 ha.

FOREIGN EXCHANGE RATES

The following conversion rates have been used, unless otherwise indicated, to change European currencies into dollar equivalents. They are "official" rates (rounded), except as noted. Except for Canada and France, these exchange rates prevailed from 1949 to 1959. For most of the period the Canadian dollar sold at a slight premium in terms of U. S. dollars. The French franc (old) has been converted to dollars at the rate of 420 per dollar in most calculations and in the various time series. In some of the calculations involving only the last years of the 1950s an exchange rate of 4.90 francs (new) per dollar has been used. When the new rate has been used, it has been noted. The new rates for the German mark (4.00 marks per dollar) and the Netherland guilder (3.62 gulden per dollar) have not been used in any calculations.

Country	Currency	Units per U. S. Dollar		U. S. Cents per Unit
Austria	Schilling	Sch.	26.00	3.85
Belgium-Luxembourg	Franc	Bfrs.	50.00	2.00
Canada	Dollar	$	1.00	100.00
Denmark	Kroner	DKr.	6.90	14.50
France	Franc	Ffrs.	420.00	0.238
Germany	Mark	DM	4.20	23.80
Italy	Lira	L.	625.00	0.16
Netherlands	Guilder, florin	fl.	3.80	26.30
Norway	Kroner	NKr.	7.14	14.00
Portugal	Escudo	Esc.	28.75	3.48
Sweden	Kronor	SKr.	5.175	19.30
Switzerland	Franc	Sfrs.	4.30	23.30
United Kingdom	Pound Sterling	£	0.357	280.00

SYMBOLS USED IN TABULAR MATERIAL

— Nil or negligible.

... Data not available.

( ) Parentheses around a figure indicate that the figure is a rough estimate.

List of Tables

List of Charts

Index

A

Accounting: methods, 58; terms defined, 59n.

Acreage control (general), 76–77

Africa cereals, 142n.

Agricultural Adjustment Act, 28

Agricultural policy (general), 25–26, 177–78, 188–90, 207; cereals, 193–94, 223; communist, 23; Europe, 31, 159; European Economic Community, 8–10, 11–12, 17, 19–21, 35, 100, 172, 184–85, 209, 217–18, 223–24; objectives, 76; problems, 23–24, 100; protectionism, 185–86; surpluses, 182–83

Agricultural product per man-year and other industries, 90(t), 91–92

Alcoholic beverage production, 112

Amino acids, 104n.

Animals, draft, 38

Argentina: cereals, 26, 30; exports, 19, 20, 26, 30, 153, 155, 176, 194n.; production, 19

Artificial insemination, 136, 170

Asian cereals, 194n.

Atlantic community defined, 245

Australasian exports, 176, 178

Australia: butter, 192; cereals, 19, 25–26, 30, 205; consumption, 102(t); exports, 16, 25–26, 30, 192, 194n., 222; livestock products, 19; subsidies, 205, 222

Austria: capital formation, 234(t); cereals, 51(t), 53–54(t), 146(f), 148(f); consumption, 103(f), 106(t), 107(t), 112, 116(t), 119(t), 127, 129, 131(t), 134, 146(f), 238(t), 239(t); corn, 146(f); costs and expenditures, 50, 51(t), 56(t), 86; deficiency payments, 51(t); depreciation, 85(t), 89(t), 234(t); EFTA, 6; exchange rates, 227; exports, 156(t); farm size, 65(t), 160; feedstuffs, 156(t), 198(t); fertilizer use, 145(t), 146(f), 148(f); imports, 154(t); land use, 60(t), 61(t), 70(f), 229(t); livestock products, 53–54(t), 106(t), 107(t), 116(t); man-year input, 69(t), 70(f), 89(t), 230(t); population, 225; potatoes, 60–61; prices, 41(t), 82, 84, 127(t), 129(t), 198(t), 218, 233(t); production and productivity, 72(t), 80(t), 81, 82, 83(t), 84, 85(t), 86, 89(t), 90(t), 138(t), 146(f), 149, 231(t), 242(t), 243(t); protection, 53–54(t); purchases, 80(t), 81(f), 83(t), 85(t), 89(t), 232(t); sugar, 53–54(t), 60–61, 112; supports, 48(t), 55; wheat, 41(t), 53–54(t), 148(f), 198(t)

Autarky as EEC policy, 10, 12

B

Balance of payments, 35–39

Barley: Canada and China, 195n.;

257

D